# SHARE AND COMPARE

## A TEACHER'S STORY ABOUT HELPING CHILDREN BECOME PROBLEM SOLVERS IN MATHEMATICS

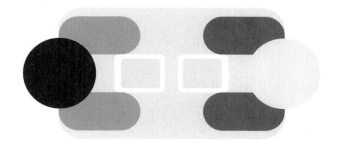

by LARRY BUSCHMAN
*JEFFERSON ELEMENTARY SCHOOL*
*JEFFERSON, OREGON*

NATIONAL COUNCIL OF
TEACHERS OF MATHEMATICS

The National Council of Teachers of Mathematics is a public voice of mathematics education, providing vision, leadership, and professional development to support teachers in ensuring mathematics learning of the highest quality for all students.

Printed in the United States of America

This book is dedicated to my wife, Sofie, and my son, Jason.

# CONTENTS

# A List of Questions

## Chapter 5: Filling the Stage: "Mathematician's Chair"

## Chapter 6: Assessing What Children Share and Compare

# PREFACE

THIS book has been written especially for teachers in the elementary grades, kindergarten through fifth grade. It should prove particularly helpful for three groups:

1. Teachers who have not included problem solving in their mathematics curriculum and want a place to start.
2. Teachers who have tried to teach problem solving but were unsuccessful and want a different approach.
3. Teachers who are currently teaching problem solving and want to add variety to their classroom practice.

Drawing on a decade of action research, I have tried to show how teachers can create a classroom environment that supports and facilitates children's efforts to solve challenging mathematics problems. The classroom model described in the following pages is offered as a framework. It represents one attempt to find a middle ground between the extremes of direct instruction and discovery learning. Any recommendations that I make should be treated as flexible guidelines, implemented according to each teacher's professional judgment and each student's needs.

In addition to describing my own instructional practices, I hope to answer these important questions:

- Why is problem solving so hard to teach and even harder for children to learn?
- What are some of the characteristics of successful problem solvers?
- What are the most useful problem-solving strategies for young children to learn?
- How can you create a balanced assessment program for problem solving?

*Share and Compare* describes my journey to implement problem solving in the classroom. Chapters 1–6 include questions and answers designed to alert you to potential difficulties and to help you address any concerns that parents may have about the role of problem solving in the mathematics curriculum. By working collaboratively with students, I have been able to formulate an instructional approach that not only meets the personal needs of children as growing mathematicians but also fulfills the curriculum requirements of my school district and state.

I encourage other teachers to start slowly rather than impose dramatic changes all at once. Begin with those parts of the model described in this book that you feel most comfortable using, then gradually add other parts. Experiment with your own variations, and share your results with others. You and your students will benefit most if you compare my observations on problem solving with your own classroom experiences.

---

# ACKNOWLEDGMENTS

THIS book is a collaborative product of many minds working together. I am grateful to several of my colleagues for sharing with me their thoughts on problem solving in mathematics and for providing me with valuable feedback during the editing process. Included in this group are Jean Stohlman, Kathy Grubb, Sue Stuhr, Wendy Bean, Mary Cunningham, Marianna Timshel, and Anita McClanahan. I also wish to thank Jean Carpenter and Ann Butterfield at the National Council of Teachers of Mathematics for their advice and guidance during the publication process of the final manuscript. But most of all, I am grateful to the many children who over the past twenty-five years have taught me more about problem solving than I could ever have hoped to teach them.

# CHAPTER
# 1
# MY JOURNEY

CALVIN AND HOBBES © 1991 Watterson. Reprinted with permission of UNIVERSAL PRESS SYNDICATE. All rights reserved.

We have arranged a civilization in which the most critical elements profoundly depend on science, mathematics and technology. We have also arranged things so that almost no one understands science, mathematics and technology. This is a prescription for disaster. We can get away with it for a while, but sooner or later this combustible mixture of ignorance and power is going to blow up in our faces.

—Carl Sagan

Unfortunately, learning mathematics without understanding has long been a common outcome of school mathematics instruction.

—National Council of Teachers of Mathematics,
*Principles and Standards for School Mathematics*

WHEN I began teaching in 1977, I could never have imagined writing this book. I thought I knew what constituted good mathematics instruction. I also was very successful at teaching children basic mathematics facts and computational procedures. Over the years, however, I have come to question much of what I once thought was true about how children learn mathematics and, more specifically, how children become problem solvers. I often recall a line from Barbara Kingsolver's book *The Poisonwood Bible* (1998, p. 505): "Everything you're sure is right can be wrong in another place. Especially here."

In 1989, I began to make problem solving the focus of the mathematics activities in my classroom. I was surprised to learn that the traditional instructional model that I had used successfully to teach arithmetic was inadequate for teaching problem solving. After many unsuccessful attempts to modify the traditional model to meet the complex demands of problem solving, I concluded that no amount of tinkering would work. I needed a new instructional model—specifically designed for problem solving—that would help children—

- make sense of mathematics,
- apply reason when crafting solutions to problems,
- learn to communicate their solutions to others clearly

and completely, and
- become confident and capable problem solvers.

## AN ACTION RESEARCH PROJECT

I began my research project in 1990 after reading *Curriculum and Evaluation Standards for School Mathematics* (NCTM 1989), as well as other books and articles on problem solving. As I tried different problem-solving activities in the classroom, a new instructional model began to emerge. I gradually began to move away from teaching problem solving as a separate topic within mathematics and toward helping children learn mathematics through problem solving.

At first, my research focused on what teachers do. This classroom model—best characterized as an instructional model—was based on a lesson format designed to teach problem-solving heuristics and strategies to children.

Over the years, however, my focus gradually shifted toward examining what children say and do. This classroom model—best characterized as a learning model—is "rich in language, where thinking is encouraged, uniqueness is valued, and exploration is supported" (NCTM 2000, p. 73).

The shift in focus away from the teacher at the center of an instructional model and toward children at the center of a learning model was a major turning point. It led to the creation of the instructional approach, which I call "share and compare," that is described in this book.

## A LEAP OF FAITH

The effectiveness of the evolving share-and-compare model was validated by working together with children. They became collaborators who verified our findings and told me what worked best. In addition, I observed other teachers successfully using the model and incorporated their suggestions for improvement. I was reluctant to make profound changes in the way I taught, however, until I read Patrick Overton's poem "Faith" (1993, p. 236):

When you walk to the edge of all the light you have
And take that first step into the darkness of the unknown
You must believe that one of two things will happen:
There will be something solid for you to stand upon,
or, you will be taught how to fly.

Fortunately, when teachers implement the share-and-compare approach they will find something solid to stand on. The supporting pedagogy is based on—

- current educational research (Battista 1999; Burns 1994; Carpenter 1999; Kamii 1989; Lester 1994; Schoenfeld, 1992; Stigler and Hiebert 1997; Trafton 1999; Wiggins and McTighe 1998);
- current research from the field of cognitive psychology (Brooks and Brooks 1993; Caine and Caine 1997; Cobb 1994); and
- current research from the field of neuroscience (Jensen 1998; Sylwester 1995).

Even more important, children acquire an understanding of mathematics that allows them to soar to new heights. Ten years ago, the children and I took a huge leap of faith when we fully implemented the share-and-compare model in our classroom. The children and their parents had to learn to trust the effectiveness of a new learning model, which was very different from the familiar one. I had to learn to trust the children and their natural abilities to solve challenging problems.

As we gradually developed these trusts, I gained new insights into how children become problem solvers. Over the years, the children have helped me learn many valuable lessons. These are the most important ones:

- Teachers give themselves teachable moments by carefully listening to children.
- Teachers give children magic moments by letting go.

## THE BLAME GAME

I have often asked, "Why is problem solving so hard to teach and even harder for children to learn?" As I struggled to answer this question, I sometimes found myself participating in what I call the "blame game." This game consists of blaming someone or something for the difficulties that teachers experience when doing problem solving with children. It has four stages.

## Stage 1

The first stage involves blaming yourself. Many teachers believe that their own lack of knowledge is the source of their difficulties. Here is a selection of typical comments made by teachers at this stage:

- "I could never figure out story problems when I was in school. How can I be expected to teach children how to do them?"
- "How can I be expected to teach problem solving along with all the other things we are supposed to cover in the curriculum?"

Teachers often try to remedy this situation by purchasing the latest book on problem solving or by attending workshops that stress the importance of teaching problem-solving strategies. However, the primary reason that many teachers experience difficulty when trying to teach problem solving is not their lack of particular skills or knowledge. In fact, I have found that good teachers of problem solving are not necessarily expert problem solvers themselves.

## Stage 2

The second stage involves blaming the mathematics problems. Here are two comments made by teachers at this stage:

- "If someone would just write some good problems, it wouldn't be so bad."
- "The wording of the problems is always so ambiguous and confusing."

Teachers at this stage frequently ask, "Who has written the book of *good* problems, and where can I buy a copy?" Although well-written problems can contribute to the success of a problem-solving program, they are not always the most important factor in helping children become confident and capable problem solvers.

## Stage 3

The third stage involves blaming children. Out of desperation, teachers say things like these:

- "My students just don't try. Unless I tell them what to do and how to do it, they just wait for me to do the problem for them."
- "Children are so impatient. Unless the problem can be solved in five seconds or less, they don't want to have anything to do with it."

Again, the real difficulties are not due to any lack of skill or ability. In fact, children appear to be natural problem solvers, since problem solving is one of the primary functions of the human brain.

## Stage 4

The final stage marks the turning point for many teachers. Either they pass through this stage and go on to learn the real source of their bewilderment, or, after blaming everyone and everything, they give up and leave this seemingly impossible task to someone else. In this stage, teachers make comments like these:

- "If the district curriculum specialist would just leave us alone and let us teach mathematics, we wouldn't have all these problems."
- "If the people at the department of education think this stuff is so easy to teach, let them come into the classroom and try to do it."

However, the reason many teachers feel frustrated in their attempts to teach problem solving is not because individuals outside the classroom are imposing unreasonable expectations. In fact, the world outside the classroom is full of problems that need solving.

This realization brings us back to the original question. If none of these scapegoats are legitimately to blame, then why is problem solving so hard to teach and even harder for children to learn?

The simple answer contains some good news and some bad news. The bad news is that it is very difficult to teach problem solving using a traditional drill-and-practice approach. Although this instructional model is effective for teaching children mathematics facts and computational procedures, it is less effective in helping children become problem solvers. Problem solving requires an understanding that goes beyond memorized facts and procedures. Genuine problem solving requires the ability to use information purposefully, not just the ability to remember it.

The good news is that effective learning models exist that children *can* use to become successful problem solvers. I have come to the conclusion that everything I was sure was right about teaching computation using a traditional drill-and-practice approach can be wrong when applied to other areas of mathematics, especially problem solving. The true blame falls on the use of an inappropriate instructional model. Problem solving becomes easier to teach and even easier for children to learn when teachers stop playing the blame game and adopt an alternative approach, such as, "share and compare."

## QUESTIONS AND ANSWERS ABOUT AN ALTERNATIVE APPROACH

### How long have you used "share and compare" in your classroom?

I have used this approach for about ten years, although the children and I continue to fine-tune it. In my personal experience, it has proved successful with children from kindergarten through fourth grade. Other teachers have used this classroom model with children at all grade levels. Readers should realize that this model has not been developed as an instructional tool for teachers. "Share and compare" is a learning model designed for use by children. This approach does not mean that the teacher should play a passive role. In fact, the teacher may play a much more active role than in many traditional mathematics classrooms.

## What did the model look like in the beginning, and how did it evolve?

At first, I approached problem solving in the same way most teachers do. I designated one day of the week as "problem-solving day" and taught problem solving as a separate topic within the mathematics curriculum. On the other four days, I continued to teach mathematics skills using a combination of drill and practice, hands-on activities with manipulatives, and mathematics puzzles or games. I did not realize that children could learn these skills through problem solving.

Later, I tried to teach problem-solving strategies, including guess and check, look for a pattern, make a list, work backward, and so on. The children practiced these strategies by solving problems that were similar to the ones I had modeled. I also taught children how to recognize key words (*altogether, less, more, how many are left*, and so on). The children then practiced applying the computational procedure that accompanied each key word. Using this approach, some children did learn how to solve some problems. However, most children did not become problem solvers capable of solving a wide range of problems with confidence.

I discovered that whenever I changed a problem in any significant way, many children would become frustrated and confused. A line of children would form at my side. Each child would say, "I don't get it." This was my cue to teach them a new strategy or key word that would allow them to solve the supposedly new problem.

When I began using very open-ended problems, I realized that young children were capable of solving problems on their own. This realization led to the practice of "mathematician's chair" (Buschman 1995), in which a student sits in a chair and uses the overhead projector to share a unique solution with peers. From that point on, the share-and-compare model began to develop more fully on the basis of two fundamental ideas:

1. Children can learn to become better problem solvers by solving problems in ways that make sense to them, sharing what they have done with others, and receiving feedback from their peers and teachers.

2. Teachers can learn to become better teachers of problem solving by observing what children say and do, then using this knowledge to extend and expand children's current levels of understanding.

## How did the NCTM's 1989 *Standards* influence the development of this classroom model?

That document was very influential. It introduced me to the idea that children can acquire mathematics skills through problem solving, rather than through drill and practice. The *Standards* document did not provide a detailed description of the classroom culture that would allow me to make problem solving the focus of the mathematics curriculum. Therefore, I created a model that would identify those details. I wanted to avoid the fate of other teachers who struggled to implement problem solving and—when they encountered difficulties they could not resolve—went back to teaching mathematics in a more traditional way.

## Do parents worry that children will not learn "the basics" if too much emphasis is placed on problem solving?

Yes. But this choice is not an *either-or* situation. It is not abandoning basics for problem solving. It is a choice between less memorization and more understanding. Nothing is wrong with using a traditional approach to teach basic facts and computation. When doing problem solving, however, teachers and children need a learning model that is appropriate for the task—one that has been developed specifically for helping children become problem solvers. If children are to learn the basics with understanding, then "their mathematics education must include much more than short-term learning of rote procedures" (NCTM 2000, p. 76).

## Are you alone in advocating this approach?

No. It has many proponents, including James Hiebert (Hiebert et al. 1997), Paul Trafton (1999), Marilyn Burns (1994), and Kathy Richardson (1997), to name just a few. However, my own experiences and the research of others reveal that direct instruction using the traditional drill-and-practice approach continues to dominate classrooms in the United States (Battista 1999; NCTM 2000; O'Brien 1999). This finding includes those classrooms that use a hands-on or manipulatives-based approach, when children complete these activities by simply following the teacher's directions.

"Well, lemme think. ... You've stumped me, son. Most folks only wanna know how to go the other way."

## When should teachers use mathematics games, hands-on activities, or manipulatives-based activities in their classrooms?

I think that such activities should be used whenever appropriate to add diversity to the types of mathematics explorations that children experience. Nothing is wrong with doing these kinds of activities. Many of them can be presented using a problem-solving format. The purpose of this book is not to tell teachers how to teach mathematics but to describe a model that children can use to learn how to become problem solvers.

## What role do manipulatives play in a problem-solving classroom?

They are one of the important tools that children use to solve problems. Rather than use manipulatives to learn a particular mathematics skill or concept, children can use manipulatives to help make sense of problems they are trying to solve.

## Why did you decide to write this book?

I often remind children, "Things only make sense when you struggle to make sense of things." This book represents my struggle to make sense of problem solving in mathematics.

# CHAPTER 2

# AN OVERVIEW OF SHARE AND COMPARE

When we memorize rules for moving symbols around on paper we may be learning something, but we are not learning mathematics. Knowing a subject means getting inside it and seeing how things work, how things are related to each other, and why they work like they do.

—James Hiebert

Building a community of learners, where students exchange mathematical ideas not only with the teacher but also with one another, should be a goal in every classroom.

—National Council of Teachers of Mathematics, *Principles and Standards for School Mathematics*

THE "share and compare" method is more than a model for learning how to solve problems. It is a culture of discourse that children create to learn mathematics with confidence and understanding. "Students who have opportunities, encouragement, and support for speaking, writing, reading, and listening in mathematics classes reap dual benefits: they communicate to learn mathematics, and they learn to communicate mathematically" (NCTM 2000, p. 60).

An emphasis on problem solving raises separate issues for children and teachers. For children, it means that they must learn not only how to find answers but also how to communicate their solution processes clearly and completely. For teachers, it means that they must devise methods to encourage children to describe what they are thinking—a request that most children find very difficult to fulfill.

When children do not show how they solve problems, our attempts to help them grow as problem solvers are thwarted. Unless we know what approaches make sense

to children, we will be unable to give them the feedback they need to improve their performance. We need to help children make their thoughts visible by encouraging them to talk and write about the processes they use to solve problems.

The remainder of this book examines the share-and-compare model and describes how it differs from more traditional approaches for teaching problem solving.

- The share-and-compare method consists of four classroom activities that can be used independently of one another. However, a synergistic effect results when all the parts are used together.
- The method can be used at any grade level.
- The method directly addresses the NCTM's five Process Standards for mathematics instruction: Problem Solving, Reasoning and Proof, Communication, Connections, and Representation (NCTM 2000).

The share-and-compare approach is a learning model that places problem solving at the center of mathematics activities in the classroom. *Principles and Standards for School Mathematics* (NCTM 2000, p. 182) describes problem solving as follows:

Problem solving is the cornerstone of school mathematics. Without the ability to solve problems, the usefulness and power of mathematical ideas, knowledge, and skills are severely limited. Unless students can solve problems, the facts, concepts, and procedures they know are of little use. Problem solving is not a distinct topic but a process that should permeate the entire program and provide the context in which concepts and skills can be learned.

## My Core Beliefs and Practices

To achieve the NCTM's vision for problem solving, teachers need a classroom model that helps children learn how to become problem solvers. Four core beliefs and five core practices guide the share-and-compare model.

## Core Beliefs

1. Mathematics is primarily a sense-making activity. Children can learn to make sense of mathematics through problem solving.

2. Children can learn how to become problem solvers by participating in a learning community whose members solve problems in ways that make sense to them, share solutions, and provide one another with useful feedback.

3. Children can learn how to become members of a problem-solving community through reflection, self-assessment, and the gradual acquisition of the qualities of good problem solvers: patience, perseverance, positive attitude, flexibility, and fluency.

4. Children can acquire the qualities of good problem solvers through a balanced assessment program that includes direct observation; interviews; rubrics; and portfolios.

## Core Practices

1. Children solve challenging problems in ways that make sense to them. "At all grade levels, students should see and expect that mathematics makes sense" (NCTM 2000, p. 56).

2. Children share solutions with partners. "Students need opportunities to test their ideas on the basis of shared knowledge in the mathematical community of the classroom to see whether they can be understood and if they are sufficiently convincing" (NCTM 2000, p. 61).

3. Children tell why they agree or disagree with their partners' solutions. From children's earliest experiences with mathematics, it is important to help them understand that assertions should always have reasons. Questions such as, "Why do you think it is true?" and "Does anyone think the answer is different, and why do (they) think so?" help students see that statements need to be supported or refuted by evidence (NCTM 2000, p. 56).

4. Children share their solutions with the class and receive feedback in the form of questions or comments. "Communication is an essential part of mathematics and mathematics education. It is a way of sharing ideas and clarifying understanding. Through communication, ideas become objects of reflection, refinement, discussion, and amendment. The communication process also helps build meaning and permanence for ideas and makes them public. When students are challenged to think and reason about mathematics and to communicate the results of their thinking to others orally or in writing, they learn to be clear and convincing" (NCTM 2000, p. 60).

5. Children compare several solutions. "Conversations in which mathematical ideas are explored from multiple perspectives help the participants sharpen their thinking and make connections" (NCTM 2000, p. 60).

Although these beliefs and practices are easy to describe, they can be hard for many teachers to implement because they represent a fundamentally different way of teaching and learning mathematics. In the United States, the traditional approach to teaching mathematics has become more than an instructional model. It has acquired the status of an institution that is accepted by many people as the only way to teach mathematics. As a result, attempts to convince such people that children can learn mathematics using a different approach can be met with much resistance.

## Questions and Answers about Share and Compare

### What are the major components of a share-and-compare lesson?

A typical lesson consists of four classroom activities:

1. Warm-up
2. Problem for the day
3. Mathematician's chair
4. Compare

These activities provide a framework that supports children's efforts to share and compare solutions to problems. When children are given "time to talk, write, model, and draw pictures, as well as occasions for work in small groups, large groups, and as individuals, students who [work] best in different ways all [have] opportunities to learn" (NCTM 2000, p. 197).

## WARM-UP

Warm-up activities, such as mental math exercises, help children acquire the conventions of mathematics. Children respond to questions posed by the teacher using a cooperative learning structure called "think-pair-share" (Kagan 1989), which can be modified to "think-write-pair-share." (See "Questions and Answers about the Warm-up.")

## PROBLEM FOR THE DAY

Children solve the problem for the day in ways that make sense to them. They work on the problem individually, or with other children, using any of the problem-solving tools available in the classroom: number lines, hundreds charts, base-ten blocks, counting tiles, Unifix cubes, pattern blocks, rulers, Judy Clocks, play money, balances, scales, thermometers, calculators, or the Internet. When children have finished solving the problem, they record their solutions using the following instructions:

- Show what you did to solve the problem using a drawing, picture, list, number sentence, or other method.
- Tell how you solved the problem using words.

Children then work in pairs, sharing their solutions with partners and telling why they agree or disagree with their partners' solutions. Children who finish before the allotted time may begin projects, such as writing a mathematics book, completing an experiment, or preparing a class presentation. (See "Questions and Answers about Problem for the Day.")

Sometimes I choose the problem for the day, but the children often identify the problem themselves. When I select the problem, I use a variety of sources, including children's literature, classroom events, the newspaper, comics, the Internet, traditional mathematics textbooks and workbooks, or other books on problem solving. Sometimes I write the problem myself; sometimes a child writes it. The goal is to challenge children to think mathematically in many different contexts and situations and to provide a rich source of material for discussion in the "mathematician's chair."

## MATHEMATICIAN'S CHAIR

The "mathematician's chair" activity is very similar to one that Donald Graves calls "author's chair" (1985). Instead of sharing their stories, poems, and essays, however, children share their solutions to problems. Graves asserts that providing a public forum to share and discuss original work gives children a chance to compare their writing with that of their peers and encourages them to provide feedback to one another. Mathematician's chair offers comparable benefits, with a focus on improving numeracy. Each child who sits in the mathematician's chair is expected to communicate clearly and completely. The children in the audience are expected to listen attentively and provide useful feedback using the following questions:

- What did you like about the solution to the problem?
- Do you agree or disagree with the solution, and why?
- How could the solution be improved?
- How could the solution be changed to arrive at a new way of solving the problem?

When a child occupies the mathematician's chair, I usually move to the side of the classroom. This show of deference encourages the audience to direct their comments to their classmate. As children finish sharing their solutions, they ask, "Are there any questions or comments?" When no more questions or comments are forthcoming from the students or the teacher, the class applauds out of courtesy and respect. The process continues until several different solutions have been shared.

In a modified version of this activity, children share their solutions orally while remaining seated at their desks or on the classroom carpet. The teacher can record solutions on an overhead projector or chalkboard and lead the discussion of each solution. These modifications may prove particularly helpful with younger children or students who are unfamiliar with this type of approach.

## COMPARE

In the final activity of a share-and-compare lesson, children compare solutions, examining both differences and similarities. To facilitate this process, children display their solutions on a chalkboard, chart paper, or an overhead projector.

## How long should each activity last?

Although the time devoted to each activity may vary from lesson to lesson, here are some general guidelines:

- Warm-up: five to ten minutes
- Problem for the day: twenty to thirty minutes
- Mathematician's chair: fifteen to twenty minutes
- Compare: five to ten minutes.

On the basis of these suggestions, an entire lesson should require from forty-five minutes to an hour and ten minutes. This guideline conforms with the NCTM's recommendation that "in the elementary grades, students should study mathematics for at least an hour a day under the guidance of teachers who enjoy mathematics and are prepared to teach it well" (NCTM, 2000, p. 371). When using the model with very young children, such as kindergartners and first graders, or with children who are new to problem solving, the time devoted to each activity can be shortened. In some situations, you may wish to schedule activities at different times during the school day. For example, the warm-up and problem could be completed at the beginning of the school day, and the sharing and comparing of solutions could be conducted just before lunch.

## Why does the problem for the day take twenty to thirty minutes if children are solving only one problem?

Although twenty to thirty minutes may seem like a long time, completing the problem-for-the-day involves several steps. First, children solve the problem in a way that makes sense. They are not simply practicing a procedure that they have been shown by the teacher. Next, they record their solutions in two different ways: by "showing" and by "telling" in words. Finally, they verify their solutions.

Each step in the solution process takes time, especially for young children or beginning problem solvers. Mathematical understanding has its price—and that price is time. I prefer to give children the time they need to construct their own knowledge rather than ask them to memorize something that makes little or no sense to them, then spend a great deal of time on review.

## Why do so many people advocate teaching children problem-solving strategies instead of asking children to solve problems in ways that make sense to children?

I think that several reasons underlie this phenomenon. First, the approach seems to be grounded in common sense. Second, much of the research on problem solving has assumed that novices should be taught the strategies used by experts. Many researchers have examined efficient ways to teach problem-solving strategies to children (Brannan and Schaaf 1991; Britz and Richard 1992; Charles 1996; Charles and Lester 1982; Forstein 1992;

Holmes, Klassen, and Szetela 1993; Hoogeboom and Goodnow 1987; Kirk 1983; O'Connell 2000; O'Daffer 1989; Reeves 1987). Third, some research has shown that middle school and high school students can benefit from systematic problem-solving instruction.

However, a review of the research also shows that teaching students problem-solving strategies does little to improve their ability to solve mathematics problems in general. Furthermore, many of the programs used to teach these strategies are not supported by sound research (Lester 1994; Schoenfeld 1992). Some of the latest research on problem solving has shown that children are natural problem solvers, quite capable of inventing their own strategies. By shifting the focus away from identifying the best methods of teaching problem-solving strategies, this research has found that children become better problem solvers by developing their natural problem-solving abilities (Burns 1992; Carpenter 1999; Mills, O'Keefe, Nelson, and Whitin 1996; Trafton 1999).

The real question is not whether children should be taught problem-solving strategies but how and when this instruction should occur. Children should be exposed to traditional problem-solving strategies as additional ways of solving problems instead of being taught that these strategies are the *only* ways problems can be solved. In other words, "mathematics teaching in the lower grades should encourage students' strategies and build on them as ways of developing more general ideas and systematic approaches" (NCTM 2000, p. 76).

Direct instruction of problem-solving strategies can take place after children have created their own strategies for solving a wide range of problems. Most children readily incorporate traditional strategies into their problem-solving repertoire after third grade, especially if they have had the opportunity to construct their own strategies first.

I should mention here that our school decided to teach problem-solving strategies to children twelve years ago. At the time, it seemed like a sensible thing to do. The practice was a natural extension of our traditional model of instruction and was recommended by many experts. We thought that this approach would be an efficient way to help children acquire the skills they needed to become problem solvers. At first, we were encouraged by the results, in that some children did learn how to solve some problems, but most children did not become problem solvers who could solve new or unusual problems. After using this approach for about three years, we realized that teaching problem-solving strategies was not an effective way to help young children acquire the characteristics of good problem solvers.

## Is it possible to use your approach without extensive teacher training?

Learning to be a good teacher of problem solving takes patience, time, and effort. Although conferences, workshops, and other types of professional development can be very beneficial, I have found that teaching problem solving is best learned by doing. You can start doing problem solving with children right away, using readily available resources. Over time, with practice and reflection, you will achieve a greater understanding of how children become accomplished problem solvers. During your apprenticeship, the following practices may prove helpful:

- Keep a detailed and accurate journal of what children say and do while solving problems or when sharing solutions. Such notes are invaluable when reviewing the day's events.

- Use a video camera to tape classroom conversations so you can see how you and the children react to one another's questions or comments.

- Ask a colleague to observe as you teach your class and to provide constructive feedback.

- Form a study group with colleagues, meeting once a month to score children's solutions using a rubric. This practice has several benefits. First, you can see the mathematics problems that colleagues use in their classrooms. Second, you can examine how children in other classrooms respond to problems. Third, you can come to a common understanding of the criteria for evaluating solutions. Fourth, you can discuss problem solving using actual student work as examples. Finally, you can support one another when difficulties arise.

- View commercially produced videotapes, such as *Mathematics: Teaching for Understanding,* by Marilyn Burns, available from Dale Seymour Publications. This set of three tapes looks at how children solve problems, reason, and communicate. Another tape available from Dale Seymour Publications is *Making Connections: Teaching and the Human Brain,* by Renate Nummela Caine and Geoffrey Caine. Although not specifically about mathematics instruction, this tape uses current brain research to suggest why traditional teaching methods often fail. You also may wish to examine a series available from the Public Broadcasting Service (PBS), titled *PBS MATHLINE: Elementary School Math Project.* These tapes provide teachers in grades 1–5 with a supplemental mathematics program that supports the NCTM's Standards. Finally, teachers in grades 3–6 may appreciate

*It Figures! Problem Solving in Measurement.* This set of three tapes is available from Pyramid Media in Santa Monica, California. Each tape presents a problem-solving situation, then allows children to compare their solutions with those of the children in the videotape.

- View the two CD-ROMs that accompany the book *Children's Mathematics: Cognitively Guided Instruction,* by Thomas Carpenter and others. These CD-ROMs, which are compatible with both IBM and Macintosh operating systems, look at children and teachers in real classrooms implementing strategies for problem solving.

## How does the share-and-compare model play out when children actually use it in the classroom?

The simplest way to illustrate the share-and-compare model is to examine some children's solutions to an actual problem and describe their classroom discussion.

At the beginning of a school year, I presented the following problem to twenty-five children in a multiage first- and second-grade classroom.

### THERE ARE 14 LEGS IN A BARN. WHAT ANIMALS MIGHT BE IN THE BARN?

I instructed the children, "Solve the problem in a way that makes sense to you." I did not provide any hints or clues. I did not show the children how to solve a similar problem, nor did I remind them of problem-solving strategies they might use.

Five of the solutions shown here are by children in the first grade (two girls and three boys); four are by children in the second grade (two girls and two boys). When examining these solutions, you will notice that no two are the same, although some are similar. In fact, of the twenty-five solutions proposed by the class, no two were identical. You should also observe that although these children were not taught traditional problem-solving strategies, their own strategies frequently resemble the familiar ones. You may recognize the following: write a number sentence (Jamie and Patrick), draw a picture (Brett, Trista, and Tim), guess and check (Marisa and Angela), use a model (Marisa), make an organized list (Taylor, Jamie, and Patrick), look for a pattern (Tim and Patrick), and use logic (Ben).

## SOLVING THE LEGS PROBLEM

### Marisa's Way

7 chickens

Marisa took two toy cows from the sorting tub and counted their legs. Then she took one more cow from the tub and counted all the legs. She took a fourth cow from the tub and again counted all the legs. She put the fourth cow back into the tub, then recounted the legs on the remaining three cows. She paused, then returned the remaining cows to the tub.

Next, she took out two sheep and counted their legs. Then she took out a third sheep and counted all the legs. As before, she took out a fourth and counted all the legs. She put the fourth sheep back into the tub, then counted the legs on the remaining three sheep. She paused, took out the fourth sheep again, recounted the legs, and with a big sigh put all four sheep back into the tub. She repeated this same process using pigs and horses.

Finally, she took out two chickens and counted their legs. She added chickens one by one, recounting the legs each time. When she had seven chickens on her desk, she counted the legs and said, "OK, that's fourteen."

At this point, Marisa looked at me as if she had finished the problem. I read the problem to her again. After looking carefully at the plastic chickens, she said nothing.

"What does the problem want you to find?" I asked.

"An animal with fourteen legs," she replied.

"What animal did you find?"

"Chickens."

"How many legs does one chicken have?" I asked.

She answered, "Two."

"So if there are fourteen legs," I continued, "how many chickens are there?" Marisa thought for a while, then counted the chickens. "It's seven chickens in the field," she said.

In this solution, Marisa has displayed many of the characteristics of a beginning problem solver. First, she used representative objects to model the problem. In fact, she might not have been able to solve the problem without using realistic models of cows, sheep, pigs, horses, and chickens. At this stage in their development, children can be very concrete thinkers. They may be unable to solve problems using traditional mathematics manipulatives or a paper-and-pencil representation.

Second, Marisa does not voluntarily describe her solution in words. In a way, she used the plastic models to speak for her. When Marisa counted fourteen legs on the chickens, she saw no reason to count the chickens themselves, since these objects clearly show their number. She did not recognize the need to count them until I asked, "How many chickens are there?" The fact that she had solved the problem seemed obvious to her, but the realization that she had failed to answer the original question was less obvious.

### Ben's Way

4 cows

Using his left hand, Ben counted on his fingers to four by touching each finger to his nose. When he reached four, he said to himself, "One." Then he used his right hand to count onward from four. He stopped counting when he had raised four fingers on his right hand, then said, "Two." He lowered all the fingers on both hands and counted on from eight using the fingers on his left hand. He stopped counting when he once again had raised four fingers, then said, "Three." He used his right hand to count on from twelve. As before, he stopped counting after raising four fingers. "Sixteen," he said, then paused before remarking, "That's too many."

He repeated this entire process twice more, each time counting beyond fourteen to sixteen. On his fourth try, however, he stopped counting at fourteen. At this point, he had raised only two fingers on his right hand, an outcome that seemed to confuse him. He repeated the counting process two more times.

After a long pause, he said, "It is four cows, but one of them is standing up with her arms waving." Later he explained that when a cow stands on its hind legs, the legs in the air become "arms that can wave at you." And we all know that arms are not legs.

Unlike Marisa, Ben did not need realistic models to solve this problem. Instead, he used his fingers as manipulatives, providing a temporary visual record of his solution process. Although his answer is unusual, it is oddly logical, reflecting a child's creative use of language.

## Angela's Way

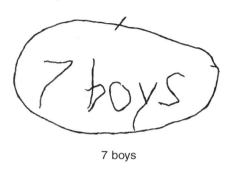

7 boys

Angela placed a handful of craft sticks on her desk. She counted out fourteen sticks and put the rest in a pile. Then she sorted the fourteen sticks into groups of two and counted the groups. When she was done counting, she wrote "7 boys" on her paper.

Next she counted out fourteen more craft sticks from the pile. She tried to arrange them in groups of three but decided, "One has two legs and the other ones have three legs, so it don't work." She then tried to arrange the fourteen sticks into groups of four. She rejected this solution, saying, "It's three horses and one boy, and they aren't the same, so it's no good."

Attempts to arrange the sticks into groups of five, then six, also failed to produce a solution. Angela's reasoning was similar in each attempt. Confronted with two groups of five and one group of four, she said, "It's no good because it's three animals, but the last one is a horse because she only gots four legs and the other starfish gots five [legs]." A distribution of two groups of six sticks and one group of two sticks inspired this comment: "It's two bugs and a boy, but they aren't the same, so it's no good." At this point, Angela circled the solution she had written previously and said, "It's seven boys."

Unlike Marisa and Ben, Angela used traditional classroom manipulatives to solve this problem. Additionally, she used a trial-and-error approach that resulted in several correct answers. However, she failed to recognize them as acceptable responses because all the animals were "not the same." Young children frequently use obscure reasons to accept or reject an answer, and these criteria can be unsettling or confusing to an adult.

## Brett's Way

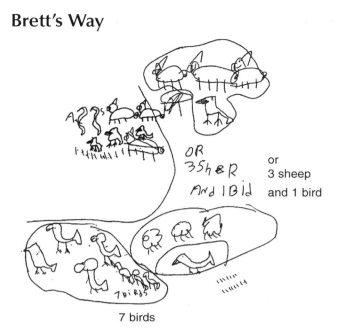

OR
35heR
And 1Bid

or
3 sheep
and 1 bird

7 birds

Brett used drawings instead of manipulatives to help solve the problem. This strategy gave Brett a permanent record of his solution process that could be examined, discussed, and reconsidered. Brett's use of drawings lessens his dependence on oral description and can improve the quality of the feedback he receives from others. His identification of more than one possible answer represents a significant step in his development as a problem solver.

## Trista's Way

Anser 1 pig
1 cow
1 horse
1 chikun

I drew 14 legs and
cownted 4 animuls.

Answer      1 pig
            1 cow
            1 horse
            1 chicken

I drew 14 legs and
counted 4 animals

Trista solved the problem with a single, highly detailed drawing, a common strategy for some young problem solvers. She also described her solution process in a brief sentence. This stage in children's development can be frustrating for teachers, since students may spend more time on the mechanics of drawing than on the mathematics in the problem.

## Tim's Way

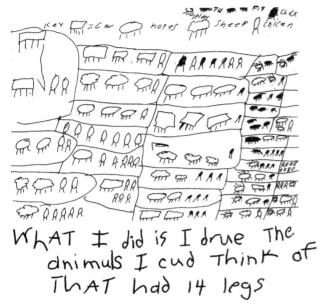

WHAT I did is I drue The dnimuls I cud Think of ThAT had 14 legs

What I did is I drew the animals
I could think of that had 14 legs

Unlike Trista, Tim represented animals using slightly abstract shapes. He identified many possible answers, recognized some patterns, and grouped similar answers.

## Taylor's Way

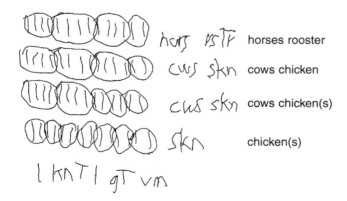

| | |
|---|---|
| hors rstr | horses rooster |
| cws skn | cows chicken |
| cws skn | cows chicken(s) |
| skn | chicken(s) |

I knTI gT vm

I counted. I got them

Taylor had come to realize that his drawings did not have to resemble the objects in the problem. In his solution, he used tally marks as symbols. Since this type of drawing can be made quickly and efficiently, Taylor had more time to think about the mathematical aspects of the problem. Although he identified only four possible answers, three of the four are mathematically distinct.

## Jamie's Way

3 horses 1 chic
$4 + 4 + 4 + 2 = 14$
7 chics
$2 + 2 + 2 + 2 + 2 + 2 + 2 = 14$
1 chic    3 pigs
$2 + 4 + 4 + 4 = 14$
3 cows 1 duc
$4 + 4 + 4 + 2 = 14$
5 ducs    1 cow
$2 + 2 + 2 + 2 + 2 + 4 = 14$
5 chics 1 horse
$2 + 2 + 2 + 2 + 2 + 4 = 14$
5 chics 1 pig
$2 + 2 + 2 + 2 + 2 + 4 = 14$
5 chics 1 lam
$2 + 2 + 2 + 2 + 2 + 4 = 14$
2 pones 3 chics
$4 + 4 + 2 + 2 + 2 = 14$
2 pones 3 ducs
$4 + 4 + 2 + 2 + 2 = 14$
2 pones 3 brds
$4 + 4 + 2 + 2 + 2 = 14$
3 dogs 1 brd
$4 + 4 + 4 + 2 = 14$
3 dogs 1 duc
$4 + 4 + 4 + 2 = 14$
3 dogs 1 chic
$4 + 4 + 4 + 2 = 14$
1 farmer 2 dogs 2 ducs
$2 + 4 + 4 + 2 + 2 = 14$
1 farmer 2 dogs 2 chics
$2 + 4 + 4 + 2 + 2 = 14$
1 farmer 2 dogs 2 brds
$2 + 4 + 4 + 2 + 2 = 14$
I rote the animls = 14
And added them up

HHHHHHH H
HHHH HHH
HHHHH HHH

HH HHHHHH
HHHH HH HH
HHHH HHH
HH HHHHHHH
HHH HH HH
HHH HHHH
HHH HHHH H

I wrote the animals = 14
And added them up

Jamie used a combination of words, tally marks, and number sentences to represent and verify each answer. She communicated her solution process effectively with an organized list. As many children do, she identified the answer "three dogs and one chick" as different from "three dogs and one duck," since "a chick is not the same as a duck."

## Patrick's Way

```
0   2   4   6   8
    ||  ||||  |||| |||||||
0    7  2s
     0 + 2×7 = 14

0    6  2s  no

0    5  2s  14
     0 + 2×5 + 4×1 = 14

0    4  2s  16
     0 + 2×4 + 6×1 = 14

0    3  2s  18
     0 + 2×3 + 8×1 = 14

0    3  2s   2 4s
     0 + 2×3 + 4×2 = 14

0    2   2s   18

0    2  2s  16  14
     0 + 2×2 + 6×1 + 4×1 = 14

0    1   2   18   14
     0 + 2×1 + 8×1 + 4×1 = 14

0    1   2   2 6s
     0 + 2×1 + 6×2 = 14

0    1   2   3 4s
     0 + 1×2 + 4×3 = 14
```

```
0 legs = snake, snail, fish
2 legs = chicken, duck, rooster, owl, bat
4 legs = pig, goat, horse, cow
6 legs = ant, grasshopper
8 legs = spider, octopus
```

```
0   3  4s   12
0   2  4s   16
     0 + 4×2 + 6×1 = 14
0   1  4   8   12
0   1  4   16   2 2s
0   2 6s   12
0   1   6   18
     0 + 6×1 + 8×1 = 14
0   1   6   2 4s
0   1   8   16
0   1   8   14   12
```

I made a list and crossed out the ones I had. I checked with a number sentence to make 14.

I made a list and crossed out the ones I had. I checked with a number sentence to make 14.

Patrick's solution is much more organized than those of most of his classmates and appears to have been directed by an overall plan. He used number sentences to explore many possible answers and recognized several that are mathematically equivalent.

## DISCUSSING THE LEGS PROBLEM

Before starting "mathematician's chair," I gave several children (Brett, Trista, Tim, Jamie, and Patrick) blank overhead transparencies on which to record their especially detailed solutions. This tactic can save valuable time during the activity. As you examine the classroom discussion, please pay particular attention to the following considerations:

• The teacher plays an important role in guiding and facilitating the discussion. I try to withhold my comments, however, until after the children have finished speaking.

• I try to keep the discussion focused on the solution process, and I encourage children to give the reasons why they agree or disagree with their classmates' statements.

• When the conversation turns away from mathematics, I sometimes step in to draw children back to the problem under consideration.

## THE MATHEMATICIAN'S CHAIR

*Mr. B.:* Who solved the "problem for the day"? Angela, will you share first? [On an overhead transparency, Angela wrote what she had written on her paper—"7 boys." Then she waited silently for comments.] Does anyone have a question for Angela or a comment about her solution?

*Curtis:* How did you figure it out?

*Angela:* I counted fourteen sticks like it says.

*Curtis:* But if you count fourteen sticks, your answer is fourteen boys.

*Angela:* I counted one-two [pause], three-four [pause], five-six [pause], like that and there was seven.

*Curtis:* You put them [the sticks] in pairs, like in twos?

*Angela:* Yeah. I counted the twos.

*Mr. B.:* Curtis, what do you mean when you say "in pairs"?

*Curtis:* In twos—like a pair of things has two.

*Mr. B.:* Everyone share with your partner something that always comes in a pair. [Students speak with their partners.] Are there other questions or comments for Angela?

*Whitney:* Did you get any more answers?

*Angela:* No. Seven boys because I counted the sticks.

*Mr. B.:* Who solved the problem a different way? Taylor, would you come up next? [While Taylor recorded his solution on the overhead transparency, I asked the other children a series of questions to keep their attention focused on Taylor and his solution.] What are the lines that Taylor is drawing? …Why is he putting an oval around some of the lines? …How many lines are inside each oval? …Do you think he will put an oval around six lines? …Why?

After each question, I waited for the children to consider their responses. Then I asked them to share three things with someone sitting beside them: (1) their answer to the question, (2) how they found their answer, and (3) why they agreed or disagreed with their partner's answer. When Taylor finished his drawing, the discussion continued.

*Taylor:* I circled four lines because they are horses and the other is a rooster. I tried some other ones and got three cows and a chicken, two cows and some chickens, and seven chickens.

*Mr. B.:* Are there any questions or comments for Taylor?

*Breanna:* How come you didn't try one cow and some chickens?

*Taylor:* I don't think it would work, because my grandpa says you can't have one cow because they take a lot of work, so you might as well have two.

*Mr. B.:* I would like everyone to try Taylor's way of solving this problem and see if one cow and some chickens will work.

*Taylor:* It works, but I still think you need two cows because my grandpa says.

*Mr. B.:* If there are no more questions or comments for Taylor, who would like to share a different way of solving this problem? Brett, would you go next?

*Brett:* I drew the sheep and the birds and stuff so it would make fourteen. [He placed his pre-drawn solution on the overhead projector.]

*Tim:* What do you mean it would make fourteen?

*Brett:* So the legs would make fourteen. Any more questions?

*Tim:* What are the ones you didn't put names on?

*Brett:* That's the snakes, and the sheep, and the birds?

*Whitney:* But that's sixteen legs, not fourteen.

*Brett:* It's fourteen because it's one-two-three-four [he counts the legs on one sheep], five-six-seven-eight [another sheep], nine-ten [one bird], eleven-twelve [a second bird], thirteen-fourteen [a third bird], and nothing and nothing [he counts the legs on two snakes].

*Whitney:* But snakes have one long leg.

*Brett:* No they don't. They don't got any legs.

*Mr. B.:* I can see that both Whitney and Brett could be correct. So when we are finished today, I would like the two of you to check and see how many legs a snake has. Report back to the class when you agree on the answer. Are there any more questions or comments for Brett?

*Justin:* I agree with Brett. I think they got no legs.

*Mr. B.:* Who has a different solution for this problem? Trista, would you share next? [Trista placed her predrawn solution on the overhead projector.]

*Trista:* Are there any questions or comments about my drawing? Because I think it is four animals because that makes fourteen legs.

*Jamie:* Did you get any other ways to get fourteen legs?

*Trista:* No, because I didn't think there are any.

*Marisa:* I agree with Trista because she draws real good.

*Mr. B.:* I would like everyone to count the legs on the animals in Trista's drawing and share with your partner what you found.

*Matthew:* She only drew twelve legs, but everyone knows a horse has four legs. You just can't see the ones that are holding up the other side.

*Mr. B.:* So when you draw a horse this way, you can't see two of the legs?

*Heather:* Like Matt says, when you draw a horse, you know the other legs are there.

*Mr. B.:* Are there any other things you can't see on the horse?

*Ben:* You can't see one of his eyes.

*Gemma:* You can't see his other feet.

*Curtis:* You can't see his other ear.

*Heather:* You can't see the half of his mouth.

*Patrick:* But his mouth don't count, because he only has one and you can see it.

*Heather:* But it's just half like the others.

*Mr. B.:* Heather, what do you mean, " … it's half like the others"?

*Heather:* Well, like she has four legs and you can only see two. So that's half the legs.

*Mr. B.:* Do you mean two legs is half of four legs? How do you know two is half of four?

*Heather:* Well, just hold up four fingers and divide it in half and you get two, like this. See half of four is two. It's two in this half and it's two in the other half.

*Trista:* Yes, because half of two is one and she [the horse] has two eyes, and so half is one. And she has one mouth, so half of one is one-half, just like Heather said.

*Mr. B.:* Will Heather's way work for the eyes and the mouth?

*Patrick:* But I still don't think his [the horse's] mouth works because it's not a pair.

*Mr. B.:* Patrick, why don't you and Heather go to the back carpet and discuss why you disagree with each other? You might also want to decide if Trista's drawing shows half of the nose and the tail. Ben, would you share your solution for the problem?

*Ben:* I think it is four cows.

*Mr. B.:* Are there any questions or comments for Ben?

*Nick:* I disagree because that's [long pause as he counts on his fingers] sixteen legs.

*Ben:* No. It's four cows because it's waving.

*Nick:* I don't get it.

*Mr. B.:* Ben, can you show Nick how you figured this problem out using your fingers? [Ben raised his left hand and held up four fingers, one at a time.]

*Ben:* One, two, three, four. [He put his fingers down.] That's one. [Ben repeated this process three more times, alternating between his right and left hands. When he reached sixteen, he realized that he had gone too far and started over. On his next try, he stopped at fourteen, with only two fingers up.] It's four cows, but only these two are his legs and the other two are arms because they can wave. [Ben raised two more fingers and moved them up and down as if they were waving at the children.]

*Breanna:* I agree with Nick. Cows have four legs, so it's sixteen.

*Ben:* But the one cow only has two legs and two arms.

*Nick:* I disagree because cows don't have arms, they just have legs.

*Ben:* No they don't. On TV cows have arms and they just walk on their legs.

*Justin:* But cows in cartoons on TV aren't animals, and the problem says what animals might be in the barn, so I don't think four cows makes sense.

*Mr. B.:* I think I agree with both Nick and Ben, because in the real world cows have four legs, but on TV some cows stand up on their back legs and use their front legs like arms. But I also agree with Justin because four legs on a cow makes more sense than two legs on a cow. Are there any more questions or comments for Ben? [No more questions are posed.] You have done some wonderful problem solving this morning, and the solutions that have been shared are very interesting. However, before we share more solutions, let's take a walk in the classroom. As you walk around the room, count the number of steps it takes to go around the room twice. When you are done, write this number in your journal. You are going to use this number for a problem we will solve tomorrow. [Young children sometimes need a break during mathematician's chair, to stretch and relax, before examining more solutions.]

*Mr. B.:* Who solved this problem a different way? Tim, would you share your solution? [Tim placed his predrawn solution on the overhead projector.]

*Tim:* There are lots of different answers. Questions or comments?

*Trista:* I agree because he found lots more than me. I think he must have them all.

*Patrick:* I disagree because some of his answers are the same. Like the sheep have the same number of legs as the pigs, so they are kind of the same. But I agree because he used bugs and spiders.

*Tim:* But it says what animals might be in the barn, and sheep and pigs are different.

*Gemma:* I agree with Tim. They are different.

*Mr. B.:* Let's come back to this question after we share a few more solutions to the problem. Are there any other questions of comments for Tim? Marisa, would you share next?

*Marisa:* I got seven chickens.

*Whitney:* How did you figure it out?

*Marisa:* I counted the legs on the animals, and I got seven chickens.

*Whitney:* But did you draw a picture or what? [Marisa brought the tub containing the plastic animals to the front of the room. She took seven plastic chickens out of the tub, placed them on the overhead projector, and counted the legs.]

*Marisa:* It's fourteen legs.

*Whitney:* I agree because seven chickens does work, because I got it, too.

*Mr. B.:* Are there any more questions or comments for Marisa?

*Matthew:* Did you get more answers or just one?

*Marisa:* The cows and sheep and stuff don't work, so it's just chickens.

*Mr. B.:* What if Marisa laid the chickens on the overhead on their sides? How many legs do you think you would see? Share your answer with someone beside you. Marisa, would you lay the chickens on their sides so we can check the answer?

*Trista:* It's kind of like my drawing because you can see one black leg but you know the other one is there.

*Marisa:* Trista's right because I can see under there when I look low. [She bends down and looks under the chickens laid on their sides.]

*Mr. B.:* Does anyone have a different way of solving the problem? Jamie, would you share next? [Jamie placed her predrawn transparency on the overhead projector.]

*Jamie:* I connected the lines like this, and then I wrote the names of the animals. I used a number sentence to check.

*Curtis:* I agree because she has all the four ways and two ways. No, wait. OK, she has them.

*Mr. B.:* Curtis, I'm confused. What do you mean by "all the four ways and two ways"?

*Curtis:* She found the animals with four legs. One animal with four legs, two animals with four legs, and three animals with four legs. Like that.

*Mr. B.:* How do you know she found "all the two ways"?

*Matthew:* Because 1 four-legged goes with 5 two-leggeds, and 2 four-leggeds goes with 3 two-leggeds, and 3 four-leggeds goes with 1 two-legged, and you can't have 4 four-leggeds because that's too much. But she got the 7 two-leggeds, so I think she got them all. [At this point, a teacher might ask the children to explore the patterns in these numbers. The patterns could also be used as part of the warm-up activity on the following day.]

*Brett:* But a farmer isn't an animal.

*Jamie:* Yes they are. People are animals.

*Brett:* No they aren't. People are people.

*Taylor:* I think Brett is right because people aren't animals.

*Mr. B.:* This is a very interesting question, and one

way to find the answer is to do a survey. I would like you to ask five adults if they think people are animals. We will share your surveys when you are done. Are there questions or comments?

*Ben:* What's a survey?

*Mr. B.:* If you know what a survey is, raise your hand. If you don't know what a survey is, look around the room and ask someone who has their hand up. Patrick, would you share your solution next? [Patrick put his solution on the overhead projector and explained how he used a list to find various combinations of animals with zero, two, four, six, and eight legs. He said that he wasn't sure whether he had found all the answers, but he thought he might have.]

*Heather:* I agree with Patrick because he tried lots of different ways and the problem doesn't say you have to find them all, just what might be in the barn.

*Angela:* But spiders have six legs.

*Patrick:* I used to think that, too, but then I found out they have eight legs because they are not an insect that has six legs.

*Mr. B.:* Does everyone understand what Patrick means when he writes "2 × 3" or "4 × 2"?

*Jamie:* It means "two times three" and that's six.

*Gemma:* But what is the ×?

*Jamie:* It means "times." Like you do it two times or three times.

*Gemma:* I don't get it.

*Matthew:* She means, say you have four and you go two times, you get eight. Four, two times, is the same as four times two.

*Mr. B.:* What Patrick, Matthew, and Jamie are describing is what mathematicians call *multiplication*, and it is a way to add numbers very quickly. If you don't know what multiplication is right now, you will someday. Be patient, there are many things that you will learn, and one of them is how to multiply numbers. Are there any other questions or comments for Patrick? [Pause] Let's give everyone who shared today one more round of applause for helping us understand this problem better. [Pause] Now let's compare the solutions that were shared. How are they alike?

*Jamie:* A lot of them used drawings.

*Curtis:* They used animals with two legs and four legs the most.

*Mr. B.:* Why do you think most of the answers are animals that have two legs or four legs?

*Heather:* Because those are the animals that would be in a barn. Like a cow or a horse or a chicken.

*Matthew:* It's the animals you see the most. You don't see insects and spiders because they are too small.

*Brett:* When I go to my grandpa's farm, I see cows and pigs but I don't see people, so I think four is good but two is no good if it's people.

*Mr. B.:* Were there any solutions that were easy to understand? What made them easy to understand?

*Breanna:* I thought Tim's way was good because he drew the pictures and made a key so you could tell what they were.

*Mr. B.:* Breanna, what is a key?

*Breanna:* When you put the names and the pictures up at the top so when you see them you know what it is.

*Mr. B.:* I'm going to put Tim's solution on the overhead transparency and point to some of the animals. When you think you know what kind of animal it is, turn to your neighbor and tell her or him how you used Tim's key to figure it out. [Pause] Are there any other solutions that were easy to understand?

*Nick:* They were all kind of easy because they showed you how they did it. But I still don't think Ben's way works, because cows don't have arms.

*Whitney:* Like Nick said, they were all easy to understand because they used stuff we could see.

*Mr. B.:* Were there any solutions that were hard to understand? Why were they hard to understand?

*Gemma:* I don't get the "timeses."

*Mr. B.:* It's all right not to get something the first time. The important thing is that you try to figure it out. If you are patient and keep a positive attitude, you will understand it. The important thing is to try to make sense of things.

*Justin:* Trista's way is hard if you don't know what's on the other side, but everybody does, so it's really kind of easy.

At this point, a teacher might choose to extend the lesson by asking children to draw a frontal view of an animal's head, so that both eyes are visible. Using these drawings, children could then explore the concept of symmetry.

Throughout the foregoing discussion, you may have noticed that the children tended to focus on the surface features of the problem. Although their comments may occasionally seem unclear to an adult, the children seem to have had less difficulty understanding one another. Young children may demonstrate a great deal of talent in solving problems but simultaneously show a real inability to identify the mathematical concepts that form the foundation for their solutions. Instead of using formal logic to explain their thinking, young children may use circular logic. For example, suppose that you ask a child, "What makes the wind?" The child replies, "When the branches on the trees move up and down, they make the wind." You then ask, "What makes the branches on the tree move up and down?" Using circular logic, the answer is, of course, "The wind."

Although children skillfully use drawings to show how they have solved a problem, their use of language to describe the solution process is frequently disorganized, unclear, and incomplete. Important steps are often left out, and mathematical terms are misused or omitted. In place of words, young children employ a great deal of nonverbal communication, attempting to let the manipulatives or drawings speak for them.

Children's problem-solving accomplishments can sometimes be characterized as "unconscious competence." They can solve problems and communicate their solutions using drawings and manipulatives, but they seem unaware of the thought processes taking place. Richard Bach, author of *Jonathan Livingston Seagull,* has written, "Answers, of course, solve nothing" (1999, p. 15). When applied to young learners, this observation can seem particularly apt. Answers to mathematics problems do not help teachers or children solve the most difficult challenges they face when doing problem solving in the classroom:

Answers do not help teachers understand children's thinking so that they can build on what children already know.

Answers do not help children make sense of the mathematical concepts and ideas embedded in problems so that they can solve unfamiliar problems in the future.

Teachers become better teachers of problem solving and children become better problem solvers when they investigate the question "Where do the answers come from?"

# CHAPTER
# 3  SETTING THE STAGE:
## WARM-UP ACTIVITIES

CALVIN AND HOBBES © Watterson. Reprinted with permission of UNIVERSAL PRESS SYNDICATE. All rights reserved.

[Children] learn by talking about what they are thinking and doing and by collaborating and sharing their ideas. Classroom discourse and social interaction can be used to promote the recognition of connections among ideas and the reorganization of knowledge.

—National Council of Teachers of Mathematics, *Principles and Standards for School Mathematics*

IN THE share-and-compare model, warm-up activities help children acquire knowledge that is accessible only from sources outside the child. Such knowledge is usually transferred to children through direct instruction, then reinforced through drill and practice. When preparing the warm-up activity, I usually ask myself the following questions:

- Will the problem for the day require specific skills?
- Will it refer to specific social conventions?
- Will it involve particular mathematical abilities (e.g., estimation, measuring time and distance, recognizing patterns, predicting the probability of events, recognizing geometric shapes, and so on)?

## QUESTIONS AND ANSWERS ABOUT THE WARM-UP

### What types of exercises do you use during the warm-up?

I typically ask the children a series of "mental math" questions. They record their answers in a journal or on a sheet of paper, then share their solutions with a partner. Here are some examples:

- What is two plus three?
- What is two minus one-half?
- What is 10 degrees warmer than 7 degrees?
- What is one-half of one dozen?
- What is twice as much as seven?
- If today is Tuesday, June 19, 2001, what will the date be this Friday?
- If it is 11:20 now and lunch starts in fifteen minutes, what time does lunch start?
- If a watermelon weighs fifteen pounds, how much would two watermelons weigh?

I also use some problems for which the answers are not immediately apparent. Here is one example:

What numbers could go in the blanks so the number sentence will make sense?

_____ + _____ = 2

Most children will give the answers $2 + 0$, $1 + 1$, and $0 + 2$. However, many other responses are possible, for example,

$$\frac{1}{2} + 1\frac{1}{2},$$

$1.25 + 0.75$, $-3 + 5$, $\$1.25 + \$0.75$, and $(1 + 0) + 1$

Some children may offer more creative answers, including 12 inches + 12 inches = 2 feet, 60 minutes + 60 minutes = 2 hours, and 5 fingers + 5 fingers = 2 hands.

### What warm-up activities are appropriate for the Legs Problem described in chapter 2?

You may wish to show pictures of two animals, such as a chicken and a cow, and ask children how they are the

18

same or different, especially with respect to the number of legs. Children could then discuss the numbers of legs on other animals and could propose answers to the following questions:

- Do most animals have two legs or four legs?
- Do all animals have an even number of legs?
- What is the least number of legs an animal can have? What is the greatest number?

Teachers can introduce scientific or mathematical terms, such as *insect, mammal, arachnid, pair,* and *symmetry.* The class can discuss words that start with *bi-* and *tri-* (e.g., bicycle, tricycle, bisect, trisect, bicentennial, tricentennial) and investigate the color patterns on national flags (many are bicolored or tricolored). Children can practice counting by twos and fours or by recognizing such number patterns as 4, 8, 12, 16, 20.

## Can you describe the process children use to share their answers with a partner?

The process is called "think-write-pair-share," which is a variation on a cooperative learning structure created by Spencer Kagan (1989). Students follow these four steps:

1. Think about the solution to a problem.
2. Write your solution in a journal or on a sheet of paper.
3. Pair with someone sitting near you, share your solution, and tell why you agree or disagree with your partner's solution.
4. Share your solution to the problem with the class.

Think-write-pair-share is a quick and easy way for all children to share their thinking with at least one other person. It differs greatly from a structure in which students raise their hands, then provide answers one at a time until the correct response is identified. This traditional practice has several disadvantages:

- If the first child gives the correct answer, no one else gets a chance to respond.
- When children give incorrect answers, they may feel embarrassed and reluctant to share in the future.
- Children who raise their hands quickly often receive more attention than children who think long and hard about the question.
- Some children learn to become inconspicuous, recognizing that someone else will eventually answer the question.

Think-write-pair-share gives all children an opportunity to respond to questions posed by the teacher, to receive feedback about their response, and to consider other solutions.

## Should the teacher record children's responses to warm-up problems on an overhead transparency or chalkboard?

This practice can help keep the lesson moving at a steady pace. Warm-up activities focus on developing fluency and flexibility, both of which are necessary traits for problem solvers.

## Tell me more about fluency and flexibility. Why are they necessary abilities for problem solving?

Fluency is an asset because problems often have more than one possible solution or can be solved using more than one strategy. Flexibility helps children apply what they know in a different manner or in an unfamiliar context. When children are solving problems or discussing solutions in the mathematician's chair, I sometimes remind them that "fluent thinkers have lots of interesting ideas, and flexible thinkers don't get bent out of shape."

One way to begin developing these traits in children uses such figures as those shown below. Teachers can display the figures one at a time, asking children, "What do you see?"

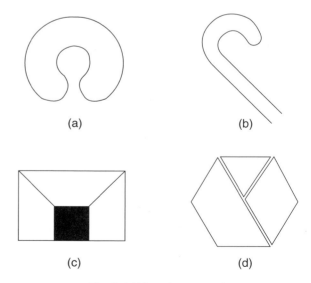

(a)    (b)

(c)    (d)

Fig. 3.1 What do you see?

Since these pictures are designed to help children think fluently, I often ask, "How many different things can you see?" At first, some children may identify only one thing. For example, figure 3.1(a) might inspire one of the following responses, but not all three: "the letter *C* tipped over," "that thing in the back of your mouth by your throat," "an angel with her hands over her head."

These pictures also can be used to help children become more flexible thinkers by rotating each figure 90 degrees, then asking, "Now what do you see?" Children who are inflexible in their thinking will often identify the same object as before.

Appendix 2 includes some other pictures suitable for this activity. Most are just doodles or enlarged parts of letters or numbers. Others were inspired by arrangements of pattern blocks or three-dimensional views of simple objects. Recently, I discovered the book *Quick Draw: Developing Spatial Sense in Mathematics* (Wheatley 1996), which contains additional drawings that could be used to develop flexibility and fluency.

# 4 LIGHTING THE STAGE:
## PROBLEM FOR THE DAY

The conventional pattern says that, first, students acquire knowledge. Only then do they think with and about the knowledge that they have absorbed. But it's just the opposite: Far from thinking coming after knowledge, knowledge comes on the coattails of thinking. As we think about and with the content that we are learning, we truly learn it.

—David Perkins

Problem solving is a hallmark of mathematical activity and a major means of developing mathematical knowledge. The challenge at this level [grades K–5] is to build on children's innate problem-solving inclinations and to preserve and encourage a disposition that values problem solving. By allowing time for thinking, believing that young students can solve problems, listening carefully to their explanations, and structuring an environment that values the work that students do, teachers promote problem solving and help students make their strategies explicit.

—National Council of Teachers of Mathematics,
*Principles and Standards for School Mathematics*

To BETTER understand the nature of problem solving, I find it helpful to consider what problem solving *is* and what it *is not*:

- Problem solving is not a separate topic within mathematics; it is a way of understanding and doing mathematics. "Solving problems is not only a goal of learning mathematics but also a major means of doing so" (NCTM 2000, p. 52).

- Problem solving is not practicing skills or strategies that have been previously taught. "Problem solving means engaging in a task for which the solution method is not known in advance" (NCTM 2000, p. 52).

- Problem solving is not about avoiding mistakes; it is about learning from them. "[E]rrors are part of the process of problem solving. If no mistakes are made, then almost certainly no problem solving is taking place" (Martinez 1998, p. 605).

- Problem solving is not just about getting the answer. It is about recognizing that problems are not really solved until children understand what they have done and why their actions were appropriate (Brownell 1946).

- Problem solving is not a solitary activity. It involves sharing ideas and comparing thoughts with other people.

When problem solving is viewed in this way, a mathematics problem is a question to which the answer is not apparent or the solution method is not known in advance (Charles 1982; NCTM 2000). In contrast, an exercise is a question to which the answer is apparent or for which the solution method (mathematics fact or computational algorithm) is known in advance. In general, mathematics problems should "serve multiple purposes, such as challenging students to develop and apply strategies, introducing them to new concepts, and providing a context for using skills" (NCTM 2000, p. 183).

The story problems that fill the pages of mathematics textbooks are not always the best problems for children to solve. In fact, better problems can be found in children's literature or in the context of the classroom. Although children should be able to solve story problems, they are not always appropriate for beginning problem solvers. Let us look at some other types, starting with "a problem within a story."

## USING CHILDREN'S LITERATURE AS A SOURCE OF GOOD PROBLEMS

Both the quantity and the quality of children's literature have increased in recent years. (See appendix 4 for a list of entertaining and useful books.) *Better Move On Frog*, by Ron Maris, was not written for use in a mathematics classroom. However, it is one of the best problem-solving books ever published. As shown in figure 4.1, the story begins with a frog examining some holes.

Holes! Lots of holes!
Which one shall I use?

Fig. 4.1. From *Better Move on Frog*, by Ron Harris

On the next page (fig. 4.2), something appears inside one of the holes, and the frog takes a closer look.

Fig. 4.2 How many animals are hiding in the hole?

When we come to this page, I say, "Isn't that interesting? I wonder how many animals are hiding in the hole?" Invariably, some children will instantly answer, "Two." Most adults would agree. For these children and adults, this question does not represent a problem, since the answer is apparent and the solution is immediately known.

For many young children, however, this question represents a genuine problem. Some children will walk over to the book, then touch the page while counting the white dots. Others will remain seated, pointing at the page while counting in the air.

In this situation, it would be a mistake to move too quickly to the next page. Although a few students may give quick responses, all children need time to solve the problem in their own ways.

Even children who have an answer may not be able to describe how they arrived at it. In problem solving, the ability to communicate your thinking to others can be just as important as finding a solution. Accordingly, teachers should routinely ask children such questions as "How do you know that?" or "How did you figure it out?"

Teachers should also resist the urge to accept the obvious answer without exploring other possibilities. Although you may agree that two animals are hiding in the hole, you should ask, "Does anyone have a different answer?" When you ask this question, you and your students will have the opportunity to experience the true excitement and joy of problem solving.

You may have to wait patiently before a child will volunteer a different answer. Eventually, someone might say, "Four—because they are turned sideways and you can only see one of their eyes." This response can make perfect sense to children, because they often draw animals as viewed from the side. For an example, you might point to the frog in the book.

Another child might say, "Four, because they are winking at you." Children in some geographical regions might suggest, "Four, because they are fireflies and those are their tails." Still other children might reason, "There are no animals, because those are holes in the back of the cave and it is the light shining through." To evoke such a wide variety of responses from children, however, you must show that you expect them to do this type of thinking and that you value their efforts.

The next page of the story reveals two animals in the hole (fig. 4.3).

Better move on, Frog.
This hole is full of badgers.

Fig. 4.3. Two animals in the hole

Before children can begin to debate who was right and who was wrong, I immediately ask, "Could there have been four animals in the hole?" Most children will agree that there could have been four. I then point out that, even though this author chose to put two animals in the hole, another author could have chosen a different number. Young children need to learn that problems often have more than one answer and that the answer they find may not be the only correct solution.

You may have noticed in the discussion of the Legs Problem in chapter 2 that children who are convinced that one answer is right may consider that every other answer is wrong. Becoming a good problem solver, however, requires not only learning to accept other valid answers but also seeking them out. For example, consider the following question:

> I have three packages of cookies. Each package holds four cookies. If I eat five cookies, how many cookies are left?

The obvious answer is seven cookies. But children have proposed other, equally correct answers, including "one and three-fourths packages," "seven-twelfths of the cookies," "fourteen halves," "seven-fourths packages," "one package and almost one more package, if he decides not to eat one and puts one back," and "the ones he didn't eat." By asking students to discover some of these less obvious responses, you can sometimes help them expand their problem-solving skills. By varying your expectations, you can sometimes elevate a question with an obvious answer to a problem with several less apparent answers.

Children's literature can serve not only as a valuable source of mathematics problems but also as an excellent resource for introducing and nurturing the qualities of successful problem solvers. Many stories written for children involve characters who must face and overcome a problem. These scenarios present good opportunities to talk about problem solving outside mathematics. To begin, you might ask one or more of the following questions:

- Did the characters use patience in solving the problem?
- Did the solution to the problem require perseverance?
- Did the characters keep a positive attitude?

As children answer these questions and others, they will begin to see the value of these traits. Although good problem-solving habits are difficult to teach, children can acquire them over time. I have found that such traits are most easily developed when they are—

- modeled by others;
- practiced in a social setting so that novices can observe, interact with, and receive feedback from more skilled practitioners; and
- experienced in a wide variety of contexts that require children to apply and use these traits purposefully.

Patience, perseverance, and a positive attitude (the three Ps) are some of the most important characteristics of a good problem solver. When I ask other teachers to describe children who have difficulties with problem solving, they offer these portraits:

- Children who lack patience and believe that if a problem can not be solved in a few seconds, it can not be solved at all
- Children who lack perseverance and who, having found an answer to a problem, fail to search for other possible answers, to verify their own answer, or to describe their solution process
- Children who lack a positive attitude and who proclaim that they cannot solve a problem, even before they see it.

Young children begin to form their beliefs about mathematics—and about themselves as problem solvers—at an early age. These beliefs not only affect their current abilities to successfully engage in problem solving but also "influence their thinking, performance, attitudes and decisions about studying mathematics in later years" (NCTM 2000, p. 76). Young children can develop a positive disposition toward mathematics by learning to trust in their own abilities and by reflecting on the manner in which others solve problems.

## USING THE CLASSROOM AS A SOURCE OF GOOD PROBLEMS

Mathematics problems that originate naturally in the context of classroom interactions and activities are especially appropriate for beginning problem solvers. Since the events are familiar to children, the problems gain a real sense of urgency and consequence. Here are a few examples of problems that have arisen spontaneously in our classroom.

### The Guide-Dog Problem

One day, our class attended a presentation by a blind man and his guide dog. During the presentation, the man mentioned that guide dogs have a working life of about six years. When we returned to our classroom, I asked the children, "How long does a guide dog usually work for a blind person?" Several children remembered the man's statement. I then posed the following problem:

> If a person is born blind and lives to be sixty years old, how many guide dogs will he or she need?

The class suggested several different solutions:

*Zachary:* What I did was I drew a dog and put how he works. I drew another dog and put how he works and it made twelve. So I did it again, and I knew it would make twelve again, and I put the [four] dogs together and I got twenty-four years they worked. So I did that again, and I put the [eight] dogs together and got forty-eight years. But that still wasn't enough. But it won't be forty-eight and forty-eight, so I just put another twelve and that made sixty. So I counted the dogs, and I think it is ten guide dogs he'll need.

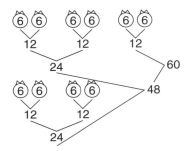

*Shanna:* I agree with Zachary, but I think it is seven dogs because a kid lives with their parents until they are eighteen, and their parents could hold their hand when they go somewhere or need help in the house. So three of the sixes is eighteen, and they don't need a dog then because she has her parents to take care of her.

*Bradley:* I agree with Zachary's drawing, but I think it's nine because he's a baby and babies don't need a dog, because he can't even walk or crawl or anything. And even if he's toddling, the dog would just drag him around on the floor. So when he's little he doesn't need a dog, but he would the other years.

*Sarah:* I agree with Zachary all the way. I think it is ten because even if he can't walk, like when he is a baby, the parents could train the dog and keep it as a pet until the kid is old enough to play with the dog and show him where to go when he is in the harness.

## The Walking-to-the-Moon Problem

One day while our class was eating lunch, Micah said to Bradley, "I wonder if we could walk to the moon?"

Bradley replied, "Of course we can't. It's just space. You can't stand up on space, it's just nothing."

Micah continued, "But astronauts do space walks, so I wonder if we could walk to the moon?"

Bradley answered, "No, Micah. There isn't any air, and you would just die if you walked to the moon."

But Micah would not let go of his question. "Look, Bradley," he said, "just pretend that we could walk to the moon. Do you think we could get there and come back?"

Bradley, realizing that Micah wasn't going to give up, said, "I don't know. It's a long way, and we would have to take a lot of food."

The next day, I posed this problem for the children to solve:

> If you started walking to the moon and didn't stop to eat or sleep, but just kept walking, how old would you be when you got back to the earth?

Most of the class solved this problem by working in groups. They walked around the school track to find out how long it takes to walk a mile, used various resources in the library to determine the distance to the moon, and used calculators to compute their answers.

## The "How Much Older Is Jared?" Problem

A high school student named Jared offered to volunteer in our classroom. As Jared introduced himself to the class, he told the children that he was fourteen years old.

When Jared was done speaking, I asked Heather, "How old are you?"

"Five," she replied.

I then asked the children to take out their journals and solve this problem:

> How much older is Jared than Heather?

Here is a selection of the responses:

*Grant:* [Sitting in the mathematician's chair, Grant raised one hand.] It's like this, you guys. Take five and you chunk it into your brain, and then you just count. [He "chunked five into his brain" with one hand, then raised the other hand to his face and began to touch one finger at a time to his nose while counting.] Six, seven, eight, nine, ten. [Grant looked confused, having run out of fingers. He repeated the process. When he reached ten, he again ran out of fingers. For several seconds, the room was silent. At last, one child whispered, "Take your other hand off your head." Grant's eyes lit up. He removed his hand from his head and continued to count. When he reached fourteen, he had nine fingers raised in the air.] See—it's nine. Do you guys have any questions?

*Stefani:* Well, what I did is I subtracted five minus fourteen and got negative nine. So she is nine less, or you could go the other way and do fourteen minus five and get nine, so he is nine more. Questions or comments?

*Shanna:* I'm seven and my brother is ten, so that's three, and fourteen is four more than ten, and I'm two years older than Heather, so add them up—it's nine. Questions or comments? [Because most of the class seemed confused, I asked Shanna to repeat her solution and asked the rest of the class to write a number sentence that would show what she had done.]

*Travis:* Fourteen is ten plus four, and five is ten minus five. So it's four up and five down, so that's nine. Questions or comments?

*Cynthia:* [Cynthia wrote "14," then "5" on the overhead transparency.] Jared is fourteen, and Heather is five." [She drew a line under the two numbers and wrote a plus sign, so her solution looked like this:

$$14$$
$$+\ 5$$

Several hands immediately went up. However, Cynthia continued to speak.] Well that makes nineteen, but Heather is not a teenager, so you cross out the "teen" and the answer is nine. Questions or comments?

$$14$$
$$+\ 5$$
$$\cancel{1}9$$

Cynthia's solution surprised her classmates. All the hands sank to the floor, along with several jaws. A murmur swept through the classroom: "How did she do that?" Although I could have viewed this situation as a mistake in need of correction, I chose a different approach.

"Isn't that interesting," I said. "I wonder if Cynthia's way would work for any other ages? Suppose Jared was thirteen

and Heather was six. Would Cynthia's way work? What if Jared was seventeen and Heather was ten? For your problem today, I would like you to find pairs of ages that work using Cynthia's way, and pairs of ages that do not work."

The next day, the class figured out how much taller Jared was than each child in the classroom, how much heavier, and how much stronger. Finally, the children wrote a book, "How Much Bigger Is Jared," in which they compared their ages, heights, weights, and strength to Jared's.

As you can see from these examples, the classroom is a fertile source of mathematics problems. The things that children say and do can provide a steady stream of problems just waiting to be solved.

## QUESTIONS AND ANSWERS ABOUT THE PROBLEM FOR THE DAY

### Can children solve problems without being shown what to do and how to do it?

Yes. Once children have been shown the conventions for recording and communicating mathematical information, they are quite capable of using this information in meaningful ways. Children can solve problems with ingenuity and inventiveness. My own classroom research, extending over the past ten years, supports this conclusion. Many other researchers agree, including the following:

- Thomas Carpenter, Elizabeth Fennema, Megan Loef Franke, Linda Levi, and Susan B. Empson at the University of Wisconsin, as documented in their recent book *Children's Mathematics: Cognitively Guided Instruction*

- Paul Trafton and Diane Thiessen at the University of Northern Iowa, authors of *Learning through Problems: Number Sense and Computational Strategies*

- Catherine Twomey Fosnot at the City College of New York and Maarten Dolk at the Freudenthal Institute, the Netherlands, authors of *Young Mathematicians at Work: Constructing Number Sense, Addition, and Subtraction (Volume 1), Young Mathematicians at Work: Constructing Multiplication and Division (Volume 2), and Young Mathematicians at Work: Constructing Fractions, Decimals and Percents (Volume 3)*

- Marilyn Burns, Alan Schoenfeld, James Hiebert, Constance Kamii, Karen Fuson, Diana Weane, Hanlie Murray, Alwyn Oliver, Pat Human, and others who have written extensively on problem solving in mathematics

- Jean Piaget, Jacqueline Brooks, Martin Brooks, Grant Wiggins, Jay McTighe, and others from the field of cognitive psychology
- Renate Caine, Geoffrey Caine, Robert Sylwester, Eric Jensen, and other neuroscientists

Children will invent their own computational algorithms to solve simple story problems (Carpenter 1999). They will also invent their own problem-solving strategies to solve complex mathematics problems. Most children do not have to be taught these strategies, nor do they have to practice them repeatedly to learn how to use them. Showing children how to solve problems can actually limit their ability to solve problems on their own (Buschman 1994; Carpenter 1999; Griffiths 1994; Kamii 1985, 1989, 1994).

## It is one thing for researchers to recognize that children can solve problems on their own, but will they do so in a real classroom?

Judging from my experiences and the experiences of other teachers who have tried my share-and-compare model, the answer is "Yes." When children understand what teachers expect—and when children learn to expect more of themselves—they can accomplish things we never thought possible. Children are sometimes reluctant to tell us their ideas because they have learned that some teachers value their ability to memorize more than their ability to think.

## Don't children need some direct instruction to be able to solve problems on their own?

Children need direct instruction in the conventions of mathematics. One of the most efficient ways for this instruction to occur is through traditional drill and practice. Children need to be shown how to write numbers, how to pronounce mathematical terms, and how to record information. But children do not need to be taught prescribed methods for solving problems. Recent brain research has revealed some important influences on brain development, one of which is problem solving. In *Teaching with the Brain in Mind,* Eric Jensen notes, "The single best way to grow a better brain is through challenging problem solving. The brain is ready for simple, concrete problem solving at age 1 or 2" (1998, p. 35). Jensen goes on to say, "Surprisingly, it doesn't matter to the brain whether it

ever comes up with an answer. The neural growth happens because of the process, not the solution" (p. 36).

## Don't children need to know how to add and subtract before they can do problem solving?

Although this opinion mirrors the conventional wisdom, I have found that it is not necessarily true. The idea appeals to those who see learning mathematics as the acquisition of sequential skills. It also satisfies some parents, since they are likely to have learned mathematics in this way. However, most young children can solve a wide range of problems without knowing how to add or subtract. In fact, young children can solve many problems by knowing—

- how to draw a picture;
- how to count; and
- how to trust in themselves and their natural ability to reason.

Instead of teaching algorithms to children so that they can solve problems, real problem-solving instruction gives children reasons to use algorithms. When they encounter quantities that make drawing pictures inconvenient or inefficient, children will naturally seek out other strategies. In this context, a computational algorithm becomes a sensible way of dealing with large numbers. In my experience, the following generalizations have proved reliable:

- Most children adopt a formal computational procedure for addition during second grade, for subtraction during third grade, for multiplication during fourth grade, and for division during fifth grade. These findings are consistent with the recommendations of the National Council of Supervisors of Mathematics (NCSM), as discussed in the report *Future Basics: Developing Numerical Power* (NCSM 1998).
- Children rarely invent computational procedures that are identical to the standard algorithms.
- Many of the algorithms that children create make more sense to them and to others than the standard algorithms taught in most schools.

Teachers often think that children do not understand basic computational concepts, because they cannot apply their knowledge of standard algorithms to solve simple story problems. In reality, "Children may actually understand the concepts we are trying to teach but be unable to make sense of the specific procedures we are asking them to use" (Carpenter 1999, p. *xiv*). In fact, children will invent many functional algorithms for computing answers to problems (Carpenter 1999; Kamii 1989).

When we wonder which comes first, computational skills or problem-solving skills, we misunderstand the difference between arithmetic and mathematics. Although most people use these terms interchangeably, they are not identical. Mathematics is a tool for solving problems; it is a way of thinking quantitatively and spatially. The ability to think mathematically leads to effective problem solving. In contrast, arithmetic is a tool for making problem solving more efficient; it is a way of using an algorithm to make computation quick and easy. For beginning problem solvers, the ability to think mathematically is essential, whereas the ability to compute is not entirely necessary.

Computation is generally what children do after they have figured out how to solve the problem. It is usually the last step in the process. Children who have been taught computational algorithms tend to see computation as the first step in the problem-solving process. As a result, they can experience unanticipated difficulties.

## What is the teacher's role in a problem-solving classroom?

The teacher's role can include the following:

- Creating a classroom environment that supports and facilitates learning how to become a problem solver
- Presenting interesting warm-up activities that build mathematics skills
- Posing challenging problems for children to solve
- Facilitating discussions and helping children understand each solution
- Modeling how to ask questions that encourage clear and complete explanations, such as "I don't quite understand" or "I'm confused"
- Conducting skill-development lessons for individual children as needed
- Using children's solutions to reinforce learned skills or teach new skills
- Modeling effective problem-solving traits and behaviors

- Asking probing and encouraging questions
- Assessing children's performance using direct observation, rubrics, interviews, and portfolios

As noted in *Principles and Standards for School Mathematics,*

> Teachers play an important role in the development of students' problem-solving dispositions by creating and maintaining classroom environments, from prekindergarten on, in which students are encouraged to explore, take risks, share failures and successes, and question one another. In such supportive environments, students develop confidence in their abilities and a willingness to engage in and explore problems, and they will be more likely to pose problems and to persist with challenging problems (NCTM 2000, p. 53).

## When children solve problems in ways that make sense to them, won't they occasionally solve problems incorrectly and develop misconceptions or bad habits?

Mistakes are certainly a possibility. However, I have found that misconceptions persist only if children do not receive constructive feedback about their solutions. The share-and-compare model helps to ensure that children receive prompt and personalized feedback, not only from the teacher but from other children as well.

Few people ask this question in reference to the traditional drill-and-practice approach, although it has been shown to cause numerous misconceptions and bad habits. Over the past sixty years, researchers have shown that—

- children make numerous errors when taught traditional computational algorithms (fig 4.4);
- children revert to their flawed practices when they do not receive continuous review; and
- children will not abandon their mistakes without many hours of repetitious drill and practice.

**Example of 'Buggy Errors':**

|  |  |  |  |  |
|---|---|---|---|---|
| The problem: | $3 + \underline{\quad} = 7$ | $\begin{array}{r} 25 \\ + 37 \\ \hline \end{array}$ | $\begin{array}{r} 52 \\ - 17 \\ \hline \end{array}$ | $\dfrac{1}{2} + \dfrac{2}{3} =$ |
| Typical student response: | $3 + 10 = 7$ | $\begin{array}{r} 25 \\ + 37 \\ \hline 512 \end{array}$ | $\begin{array}{r} 52 \\ - 17 \\ \hline 45 \end{array}$ | $\dfrac{1}{2} + \dfrac{2}{3} = \dfrac{3}{5}$ |

Fig 4.4. Computational errors made using the drill-and-practice approach

For more information on this topic, teachers may wish to consult the following references:

- Constance Kamii, *Young Children Continue to Reinvent Arithmetic, 3rd Grade* (New York: Teachers College Press, 1994).
- Thomas Carpenter et al., "A Longitudinal Study of Invention and Understanding in Children's Multidigit Addition and Subtraction," *Journal for Research in Mathematics Education* (January 1998): 3–20.
- Constance Kamii and Ann Dominick, "The Harmful Effects of Algorithms in Grades 1–4," in Lorna Morrow and Margaret Kenney, eds., *The Teaching and Learning of Algorithms in School Mathematics, 1998 Yearbook* (Reston, VA: National Council of Teachers of Mathematics, 1998): 130–40.

## Since children are only solving one problem each day, how do they get enough practice in basic mathematics skills?

Although problem solving is the focus of our mathematics classroom, children also engage in skill-development activities. Such activities may occur at different times throughout the school day. For example, students learn specific skills when—

- participating in warm-up activities;
- completing drill-and-practice exercises;
- playing mathematics games and solving mathematics puzzles;
- participating in hands-on explorations with manipulatives;
- receiving direct skills instruction from the teacher; and
- practicing mathematics skills in other subjects.

## Should the problem for the day be read to children?

Reading the problem aloud is usually a good idea. It helps those children who are poor readers, and gives all children a chance to ask better questions about the problem. Teachers also may want to help children recognize the various parts of a problem, so they can use this knowledge when writing their own problems.

## What do you do after you are done reading the problem to the children?

I usually move away from the front of the classroom. This act of stepping aside sends a very clear message concerning the roles and responsibilities of the teacher and children in a problem-solving classroom. It reinforces the expectation that children should solve the problem in ways that make sense to them. It also lets children know that I have confidence in their abilities to meet this expectation.

Some children will not expend the effort required to solve challenging problems if their teacher is standing by, ready to tell them what to do when they encounter difficulties. Other children may not be willing to take risks, make mistakes, or try new solutions, if a teacher is looking over their shoulders. Once children have started their solutions to the problem, I move around the room and begin interacting with them.

## What is the teacher's role while children are actually solving the problem?

This question is difficult to answer, since the role of facilitator requires a great deal of knowledge and intuition. It is hard to know when to step in and when to step back, when children genuinely need assistance and when it is better to simply leave them alone. This decision requires professional judgment, along with specific knowledge about each child and his or her abilities as a problem solver. In general, teachers can support learning by—

- assessing the mathematical skills and abilities of children and using this information to select appropriate warm-up activities, to pose problems that are neither too easy nor too difficult, and to provide timely direct instruction;
- modeling appropriate use of mathematical terms;
- asking perceptive questions that illuminate difficulties and inspire understanding; and
- providing children with access to the tools and materials they need to solve problems.

As many educators agree,

When challenged with appropriately chosen tasks, students become confident in their ability to tackle difficult problems, eager to figure things out on their own, flexible in exploring mathematical ideas and trying alternative solution paths, and willing to persevere. Students should view the difficulty of complex mathematical investigations as a worthwhile challenge rather than as an excuse to give up (NCTM 2000, p. 21).

## Do you ever help children with their solutions to the problem?

Yes, but it is not the kind of assistance that I used to provide. Rather than give help or clues, I now ask questions, in an attempt to better understand why children are having difficulties, and to help children resolve those difficulties themselves. I have found that showing children what to do can deprive them of the opportunity to make their own mathematical discoveries—and to experience the personal satisfaction that comes with these insights. "When students work hard to solve a difficult problem or to understand a complex idea, they experience a very special feeling of accomplishment, which in turn leads to a willingness to continue and extend their engagement with mathematics" (NCTM 2000, p. 21). Nevertheless, teachers can find it very hard not to help in the traditional way. Several reasons can be cited for this incongruity:

- Much of their training has prepared teachers for the role of professional helper; it is what many parents and children expect teachers to do. However, I have found that the kind of help teachers often give children is not the kind of assistance that children need if they are to grow as problem solvers. When children solve problems in ways that make sense to them, they acquire new knowledge and make new connections with what they already know. These connections are precisely the help that children need to learn mathematics with understanding.
- Many teachers do not know how to ask questions that encourage children to think for themselves. They know only how to tell children what to do. As a result, their questions are designed to ensure that children mimic the teacher's thinking.

"Teachers must recognize that [children] can think in sophisticated ways, [and that they are] resourceful individuals who construct, modify, and integrate ideas by interacting with the physical world and with peers and adults" (NCTM 2000, p. 75).

## Do all children solve the same problem?

Although children occasionally solve different problems in my classroom, asking them to solve the same problem provides a common topic for discussion. Instead of assigning different problems, I prefer to vary my expectations for the given problem. For example, I might expect some children to find multiple solutions or to solve the problem in more than one way.

In some situations, it may be appropriate to pose slightly different versions of the same problem. Here are some suggestions for this technique:

- Vary the quantities in the problem. Larger numbers or fractional quantities usually make the problem more difficult (see fig 4.5).

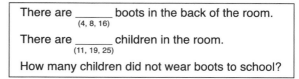

Fig. 4.5. Varying quantities in a problem

- Alter the question asked. Many problems appropriate for young children can be thought of in terms of three variables and one operation. The corresponding number sentence might be written as

$$x \; (\;) \; y = z,$$

where the parentheses ( ) enclose any of the four arithmetic operations. In my experience, some young children find solving for $z$ less difficult than solving for $x$ or $y$ (see fig. 4.6).

Many problems can be thought of in terms of three variables and one operation: $x \; (\;) \; y = z$:
- It takes 2 minutes to walk around the track. If I go around the track 5 times, how long will I walk?
- It takes 2 minutes to walk around the track. If I walk for 12 minutes, how many times did I go around the track?
- I walked around the track 8 times. If it took 16 minutes, how long did it take to go around the track once?

Fig. 4.6. Altering the question

- Change the degree to which children can model the actions described in the problem (Carpenter 1999). Problems frequently become more difficult when children can not directly model such actions (see fig. 4.7).

| | | | |
|---|---|---|---|
| **Join** | **Result Unknown**<br>Mrs. B. has 3 cats. A friend gives her 2 more cats. How many cats does she have now? | **Change Unknown**<br>Mrs. B. has 3 cats. How many more does she need to adopt to have 5 cats in all? | **Start Unknown**<br>Mrs. B. has some cats. She gets 2 more for her birthday. Now she has 5 cats. How many did she have before her birthday? |
| **Separate** | **Result Unknown**<br>Mrs. B. has 5 cats. She gave 2 cats to a friend. How many cats does she have left? | **Change Unknown**<br>Mrs. B. has 8 cats. Some of them are hiding. If she can see 3 cats, how many are hiding? | **Start Unknown**<br>Mrs. B. some cats. She gets 2 more for her birthday. Now she has 5 cats. How many did she have before her birthday? |
| **Part-part-whole** | **Whole Unknown**<br>Mrs. B. has 6 black cats and 3 white cats. How many cats does she have? | **Part Unknown**<br>Mrs. B. has 8 cats. 3 are white cats, and the rest are black cats. How many are black cats? | |
| **Compare** | **Difference Unknown**<br>Mrs. B. has 8 white cats and 5 black cats. How many more white cats does she have than black cats? | **Compare Quantity Unknown**<br>Mrs. B. has 3 white cats. She has 5 more black cats than white cats. How many black cats does she have? | **Reference Set Unknown**<br>Mrs. B. has 8 cats. She has 3 more white cats than black cats. How many black cats and how many black white cats does she have? |
| **Grouping** | **Multiplication**<br>Each of Mrs. B's. 3 cats had 5 kittens. How many kittens does she have? | **Measurement Division**<br>Mrs. B. has 15 kittens. She put 3 kittens at each bowl of food. How many bowls did she use? | **Partitive Division**<br>Mrs. B. has 15 kittens and 5 bowls of food. If she puts the same number of kittens at each bowl, how many kittens will eat out of each bowl? |

Fig. 4.7. Changing the degree to which children can model actions in a problem (adapted from Carpenter et al. [1999])

• Vary the number of parts to the problem. Problems can be more difficult when children must answer more than one question (see fig. 4.8).

---

Problems can be thought of in terms of how many questions are asked or how many layers of difficulty are presented.

• Jason earns money by mowing lawns. He gets paid $3.00 for each lawn he mows and $2.00 for each lawn he edges. How much will he earn if he mows and edges 4 lawns?

• If Jason mows 6 lawns each weekend, and only edges half of them, how much will he earn this month?

• If Jason earned $23.00 last month, how many lawns did he mow and how many did he edge?

---

Fig. 4.8. Adding questions to a problem

• Change the level of abstraction in the problem. Problems that require young children to work with minutes, pounds, or inches are sometimes more difficult to solve than problems dealing with cookies, cars, or cats.

• Vary the number of steps required to solve the problem. Two-step or three-step problems are sometimes more difficult than single-step problems.

# What if the children can't get started on their own?

My first advice is to be very patient. Some children may reveal an initial reluctance to solve problems on their own. Unaware of their own problem-solving abilities, they may expect their teacher to show them what to do. Other children can be reluctant to solve problems in ways that make sense to them because they are afraid of making mistakes. They may not realize that—in a problem-solving classroom—teachers value mistakes just as much as correct answers. You can overcome many of these misgivings by showing examples of how other children have solved problems.

You also may wish to share this advice with the class:

If you don't know what to do, draw a picture of what you know.

Teaching children this axiom serves several purposes:

• Children know what to do, even when they don't know how to solve a problem.

• Drawings help children organize their thoughts.

• Drawings can be helpful with a wide range of problems.

- Most children can learn to make drawings quickly and easily.
- After completing their drawings, children are often surprised by the ease with which they can identify solutions.
- "The use of [drawings] provides a further opportunity for understanding and conversation. Having a concrete referent helps develop understandings that are clearer and more easily shared" (NCTM 2000, p. 97).
- Drawings "can carry some of the burden of remembering by letting students record intermediate steps in a process" (NCTM 2000, p. 138).

## What about children who can get the answer but have trouble describing their process in words?

Teachers of young children often discover the truth in the cartoon above. Many children experience difficulty describing their solution process in words. This issue has created some debate among teachers of problem solving. Some teachers think that students (K–2) should not always be expected to record their solution process using words. According to this view, "putting too much emphasis on children's production of products can take away time needed for active involvement with tasks" (Richardson 1997, p. 100). Instead of asking children to write about what they have done, these teachers prefer to have children solve additional problems, and then talk about their solutions.

Other teachers believe that unless children learn to describe their solutions in writing, they will not become fluent problem solvers. Such teachers often accept whatever the child produces, then build on that output, as in a writers' workshop (Burns 1995). They remind children that writing helps to clarify thinking, and they remind teachers that written solutions provide valuable insights. For example, written responses can be useful tools for designing lesson plans and assessing student performance.

Since this issue remains unresolved, teachers should consider it carefully. However, we should also remember that this disagreement is not an either-or situation. Children can engage in developmentally appropriate tasks that accomplish the goals of both groups. For example, they can describe their solution processes to a scribe, or record their work on audiotape. As children learn to share their solutions orally—through think-write-pair-share or the mathematician's chair, they will develop many of the skills necessary for producing written responses.

As the mathematics curriculum expands to encompass the entire range of skills included in *Principles and Standards for School Mathematics* (NCTM 2000), the solution process becomes as important as the answer to the problem. Answers alone often fail to reveal the quality of children's thinking and the level of their understanding, both of which are more accurately revealed through children's written or oral descriptions of how they solved the problem.

When children commit thoughts to words, they take the first steps toward learning to communicate mathematically. Both oral and written forms of communication help children reflect on their understandings, make connections, and internalize mathematical concepts. When children discuss mathematical information, they remember it better, understand it more fully, and begin to use it to uncover even more information (Perkins 1992). Through sharing, children "realize that representing, discussing, reading, writing, and listening to mathematics are a vital part of learning and using mathematics" (NCTM 1989, p. 26).

## What about young children who can't write?

Although some children may not yet be able to write, almost all children can do the following:

- Draw pictures that represent their solutions to the problem
- Use manipulatives to solve a problem, then draw pictures of what they have done
- Talk about their solutions.

## What about older children who have trouble describing what they have done?

Since the development of oral language usually precedes the development of written language, children should be given frequent opportunities to discuss their mathematical thinking with others. In real estate, as the saying goes, the three most important things are location, location, location. In problem solving, the three most important things are talk, talk, talk—and the children should do most of the talking. While helping children become capable problem solvers, the share-and-compare model also helps them become fluent in the language of mathematics. Children learn this language by using it.

- Encourage children to talk about problems before, during, and after the time allotted for solving problems. One of Spencer Kagan's cooperative learning structures (1989) may enhance or facilitate these discussions (see fig. 4.9). In the past, good arithmetic classrooms were places where children worked silently at their desks. Good problem-solving classrooms are busy places where children participate in lively discussions with their teacher and peers.

- Engage children in a variety of writing activities, such as drafting letter problems (fig. 4.10), reporting news stories, justifying scores that they determined using a rubric, or explaining the selection of items in their portfolios.

---

### Cooperative Learning Structures (Kagan 1989)

**Corners**
- Description: Each student moves to a corner of the room representing a teacher-determined alternative. Students discuss within corners, then listen to, and paraphrase ideas from, other corners.
- Functions: Seeing alternative hypotheses, values, problem-solving approaches, knowing and respecting different points of view, meeting classmates

**Match Mine**
- Description: Students attempt to match the arrangement of objects on a grid of another student using oral communication only.
- Functions: Vocabulary development, communication skills, role-taking ability

**Numbered Heads Together**
- Description: The teacher asks a question, students consult to make sure everyone knows the answer, then one student is called on to answer.
- Functions: Review, checking for knowledge, comprehension, tutoring

**Pairs Check**
- Description: Students work in pairs within groups of four. Within pairs students alternate—one solves a problem while the other coaches. After every two problems the pair checks to see whether they have the same answers as the other pair.
- Functions: Practicing skills, helping, praising

**Think-Pair-Share**
- Description: Students think to themselves on a topic provided by the teacher; they pair up with another student to discuss it; they share their thoughts with the class.
- Functions: Generating and revising hypotheses, inductive reasoning, deductive reasoning, application, participation, involvement

**Team Word-Webbing**
- Description: Students write simultaneously on a piece of chart paper, drawing main concepts, supporting elements, and bridges representing the relation of ideas.
- Functions: Analysis of concepts into components, understanding multiple relations among ideas, differentiating concepts, role taking

Fig. 4.9. Cooperative learning structures (adapted from Kagan [1989])

**Description:** Children or adults write and publish an original problem in the form of a letter. Other children select a Letter Problem they wish to solve, then mail the solution to the author using an in-school delivery system. The author reads each solution and sends a written reply to each person who attempts the problem.

**Directions for children who write a Letter Problem:** (1) Write five original story problems. (2) Meet with two other children, and choose the best problem. (3) Publish your problem in the form of a letter, then place several copies in the chosen classroom. (4) Read all solutions, and write a reply to each person, telling them why you agree or disagree with the solution.

**Directions for children solving a Letter Problem:** (1) Take one of the Letter Problems from the display. Show how you solved the problem, and tell what you did to find your answer. (2) Mail your solution to the author using the in-school delivery system. (3) In a few days, you will receive a reply from the author.

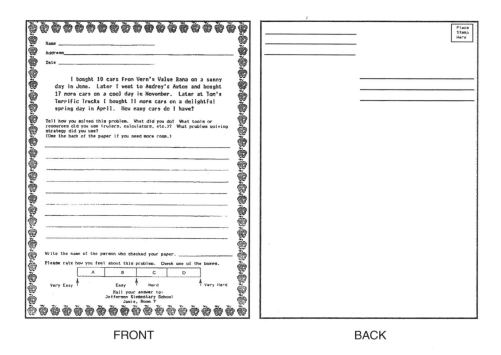

FRONT                    BACK

Fig. 4.10. Instructions for a letter problem

- Teach children how to make diagrams, charts, tables, or graphs, which they can use to help describe their problem-solving processes.
- Ask children to record their solutions on audiotape, listen to their own recordings, and transcribe their own words.
- Allow children to think aloud by talking softly to themselves as they solve a problem.

## What about a child who describes the solution process by saying, "I did it in my head"?

Typically a few children in each class volunteer this explanation. In some situations, it doesn't help to ask them to describe what they have done in their heads; they may not be able to tell you. The real source of the difficulty may be the mathematics problem itself. If it did not meet the definition of a genuine problem, the answer may have been apparent or the solution immediately known. My usual remedy is to offer a more challenging version of the problem.

## What do you do if none of the children can solve the problem?

Temporary setbacks can provide exciting problem-solving opportunities. When an impasse occurs, I announce, "This problem must be really good, and anyone who can solve it must be a very good problem solver."

You should remind children that good problems take time to solve. Problem solvers need to be patient and perseverant. They also need to keep a positive attitude.

You may be able to identify the source of the difficulties by asking questions (fig. 4.11). Further questioning can help children move on with their solutions.

If this strategy fails, ask children to set the problem aside and start a different activity. It may help to take a break or go to recess. I might tell the children, "Since this problem is so good, we need more time to think about it." We might wait until after recess—or perhaps until the next day—before resuming work on it.

---

### Probing Questions

- Can you tell me what the problem is about?
- Can you say the problem in your own words?
- What do you know?
- What does the problem want you to find?
- Do you understand each of the words in the problem?
- What is the important information in the problem? Is some information unnecessary or missing?
- What did you do first? Why?
- What does your drawing of the information in the problem look like?
- What manipulatives have you tried to use to solve the problem?
- Would making a list, table, chart, or graph help you solve this problem?
- Can you tell me how your plan for solving this problem will work?
- How is this problem like others you have solved?
- Does your show-and-tell include all the steps in your solution?
- Did you label your drawing or include a key?
- Have you shared your solution with someone else?

Fig. 4.11. Questions for problem solvers

## What should children do while they are waiting for others to finish the problem?

I use a wide variety of activities in order to add diversity and novelty to classroom routines. Children may solve another problem, or continue to work on individual projects, such as writing a book on a mathematical topic (see appendix 3), designing a mathematical game, or conducting another interesting investigation. Figure 4.12 lists several ideas for mathematics projects.

---

### More Ideas for Projects

**Car Show**
1. Build a car that does something special or unique.
2. Use only recycled materials.
3. Write a story about what your car can do and why it is special.
4. How fast can your car go?
5. What is the diameter of the tires on your car?

Building materials: cardboard (cereal boxes, paper tubes), cans, pieces of wood, egg cartons, pieces of plastic, paper, and anything found at home that you can use.

**Fantastic Flyers**
1. Make something that flies.
2. Measure how high your flier can fly.
3. Measure how far your flier can fly.
4. Record your measurements for at least 10 flights.
5. Write a description of how well your flier flies and any special tricks it can do.

Building materials: same as above for Car Show

**Wild Animal Habitat Show**
1. Pick a wild animal.
2. Find out as much as you can about this animal and the place where it lives.
3. Make a display showing the animal in its habitat.
4. Write a description of your display. Include lots of mathematical information (weight, height, speed, etc.).

Building materials: same as above for Car Show

**Home Show**
1. Think about what your ideal home would be like.
2. Design a floor plan for your dream home.
3. Build a model of your house out of reused material.
4. Write a description telling what makes your house special.

Building materials: same as above for Car Show

Fig. 4.12. Suggested mathematics projects

You can also establish stations or centers in the classroom, where children record the results of their investigations on a data sheet (fig 4.13). The version shown here provides space to record the following information:

- The day, the date, the number of days since the beginning of the school year, and the number of days remaining
- Date equations (number sentences that equal the date)
- Current weather information (determined using a classroom weather station)
- A prediction for the next day's weather
- The current time
- The amount of money in three different cups

- An estimate for the quantity, weight, or length of a group of objects
- The actual weight of an object or group of objects

**Data Sheet for a Station/Center**

Fig. 4.13. Data sheet

Your decisions in this situation will depend on both student and classroom goals. Some teachers may allow children to select their own activities, or use this time for other subjects in the curriculum. For more detailed descriptions of mathematics projects, you may wish to consult "A Teacher's Journal: Boy Do I Have Problems!" (Buschman 1996) or the *MEGA Projects* series available from Dale Seymour Publications.

## How do you keep problem solving interesting?

Just as the two gentlemen are drawn into the problem in the cartoon above, I have found that using a wide variety of problems can keep children interested and engaged. As I mentioned earlier in this chapter, both children's literature and classroom events can provide intriguing problems. But there are many other possible sources, including those listed below:

- Traditional mathematics books [I modify these problems using "communication structures" (Buschman 1995). A list of communication structures appears in appendix 5.1.]
- Children themselves (see examples in appendix 5.2)
- Newspaper articles or comics (see appendix 5.3)
- The Internet (see appendix 5.4)
- Books on problem solving (see appendix 5.5).

## What are your top ten problems for children to solve?

My top ten problems all share these characteristics:

- They are very open-ended.
- They ask children to use the language of mathematics.
- They can be used over and over again, simply by changing certain details.

When I use one of these problems as a warm-up activity, I ask children to write as much as they can in a specific amount of time, typically from two to five minutes. When used as the problem for the day, I frequently ask children to write as many solutions as possible. In no particular order, here are my top ten problems:

1. Write ten things you know about the number _____. (Figs. 4.14a and b show student responses for the number 10. Other interesting possibilities include: 5, 1/2, −32, $3.50, 7:00, and 1998.)
2. Write the names of ten places where you can find a(n) _____. (The following items have all provoked interesting responses: triangle, odd number, right angle, 3 in the tens digit.)
3. Write ten things that this graph/table/picture/chart tells you. Or write ten questions that someone could answer using the information on this graph/table/picture/chart. (Fig. 4.15 shows a student's response for a graph.)
4. Write and publish a Letter Problem. (See fig. 4.10.)
5. Solve a What Do You See? problem. (Examples appear in figs. 3.1–4 and appendix 2.)
6. Write a plan for how you could figure out the number of _____ without counting them. (The

following items have worked well for this problem: children in our room, children in our school, pencils in our classroom, shoes in our classroom, children on your bus.)

7. Which one of the four items doesn't belong? Why doesn't it belong? What does belong?

(Fig. 4.16 shows student responses for the numbers 6, 10, 12, 15. You may also wish to try fractions, clock faces, coins, or other items.)

8. How would you describe this design to a friend over the telephone? (Pattern blocks, tiles, wallpaper samples, and cloth samples are all good sources of designs.)

9. How could you measure a _____? (Some possibilities include: a shadow, a puddle, a hot dog, a bedroom, and a balloon.)

10. How is a _____ like a _____, and how are they different? (I have used many different pairs of items in this problem, including one and seven, triangle and rhombus, fraction and decimal number, ruler and clock.)

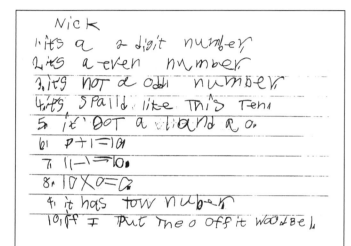

Nick

It's a 2 digit number.

It's a even number.

It's not a odd number.

It's spelled like this ten.

It got a 1 and a 0.

9 + 1 = 10.

11 − 1 = 10.

10 × 0 = 0.

It has two number(s).

If I put the 0 off it would be 1.

Fig. 4.14a. Nick's solution for "Write ten things you know about 10."

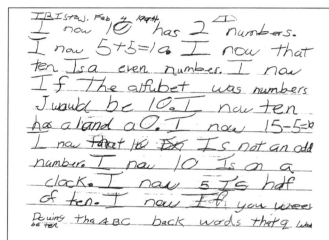

Trista

I know 10 has 2 numbers.

I know 5 + 5 = 10.

I know that 10 is a even number.

I know if the alphabet was numbers J would be 10.

I know ten has a 1 and a 0.

I know 15 − 5 = 10.

I know that 10 is not an odd number.

I know 10 is on a clock.

I know 5 is half of 10.

I know if you were doing the ABC backwards that Q would be ten.

Fig. 4.14b. Trista's solution for "Write ten things you know about 10."

## Examples of problems authored by a child using a graph

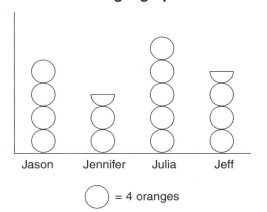

Jason    Jennifer    Julia    Jeff

◯ = 4 oranges

How many oranges did Jason eat?

How many more oranges did Julia eat than the rest of them?

Who ate more the boys or the girls?

How many oranges did they all eat?

How much is ⌣ ?

The kids put the oranges in a bag. The oranges weigh 1 pound. How much does the bag weigh?

Julia gave half her oranges to Jeff so how much do they each have?

Oranges are 25 cents at Rick's Market so how much did Jeff spend?

A glass of orange juice is two oranges. How many glasses of juice did Jennifer make with all her oranges?

How do they make the oranges sit on top of each other?

Fig. 4.15. Whitney's response to "Write ten questions that someone could answer using the information on this graph."

## Which number doesn't belong with the others? Why?

**Sample student responses:**

*Marisa:* I think it is 6 because 6 is a little number and the rest are big numbers.

*Todd:* I think it is 6 because it is one digits and the others are 2 digits.

*Breanna:* I think it is 6 because if you make it turn over you get a 9, but if you turn over 10, 12, and 15, you don't get anything.

*Jose:* I think it is 15 because 15 is odd and the others are even.

*Stephanie:* I think it is 15 because you can't cut it in half like you can cut 6 in half and get 3, and cut 10 in half and get 5, and cut 12 in half and get 6, but you cut 15 in half and what do you got.

*Taylor:* I think it is 15 because 15 is not on the clock and 6, 10, 12 are on the clock.

*Tanisha:* I think it is 10 because when you count by 3s you don't say 10.

*Patrick:* I think it is 10 because if you spell it backwards it makes a word, net. But if you spell the others backwards you won't get a word.

*Sarah:* I think it is 10 because it rhymes with a lot of words like men, Ben, hen, when, pen, den, Ken and 6, 15, 12 don't rhyme with very many words. Well, I guess 6 does like fix and sticks but I still don't think it rhymes with as many as 10.

*Joel:* I think it is 12 because it gots an even number of letters and the others gots an odd number of letters.

*Katrina:* I think it is 12 because if you go 6, 6, 6, 6, 6 you get 30, and if you go 15, 15 you get 30, and if you go 3, 3, 3, 3, 3, 3, 3, 3, 3, 3 you get 30, but 12 don't get 30.

*Tim:* I think it is 12 because it is wrong there; [it] should be 19 because then it would count 4 on the sides and 9 on the top and bottom $[10 - 6 = 4; 19 - 15 = 4; 15 - 6 = 9; 19 - 10 = 9]$.

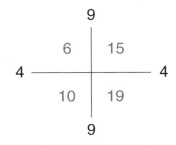

Fig. 4.16. Student responses to "Which number doesn't belong?"

# 5 FILLING THE STAGE:
## "MATHEMATICIAN'S CHAIR"

© Lynn Johnston Productions, Inc. Reproduced by permission.

Learning with understanding can be further enhanced by classroom interactions, as students propose mathematical ideas and conjectures, learn to evaluate their own thinking and that of others, and develop mathematical reasoning skills.

> —National Council of Teachers of Mathematics,
> *Principles and Standards for School Mathematics*

**B**EFORE answering specific questions about the "mathematician's chair," an examination of children's solutions to another problem might be helpful. I presented this problem later in the school year to the same twenty-five children who solved the Legs Problem described in chapter 2.

> Mr. B wants to give two cards to everyone in the classroom.
> There are five cards in each package.
> How many packages does he need to buy?

As before, I asked the children to "solve the problem in ways that make sense." I gave them no other directions, hints, clues, or reminders.

## SOLVING THE CARDS PROBLEM

Most adults probably would solve this problem using a traditional algorithm. Only one of the children (Tim) chose this approach. However, many children used recognizable versions of traditional problem-solving strategies, although such strategies had not been taught to them. These strategies included—

- write a number sentence (Tim),
- draw a picture (Ben),
- guess and check (Taylor),
- make a model (Jamie),
- make an organized list (Trista),
- act it out (Angela),
- look for a pattern (Patrick), and
- use logic (Brett).

## MARISA'S WAY

Marisa 1-19-1994

I got 59 cards and 25 kids.

I put a lot of circles for heads.

59 packages

38

Marisa attempted to model this problem using counting tiles and cubes. First she determined the number of children in the classroom in a very interesting way. Instead of actually counting the children, she counted the children's portfolio crates. Then she represented the children with twenty-five cubes. Next she placed two tiles under each cube and began to count the tiles. Many children will attempt to use only one manipulative when solving a problem. As a result, they sometimes miscount. Marisa avoided this potential source of error by using different manipulatives to represent the children and the cards.

When considering Marisa's solution, a teacher may have difficulty recognizing the things that she has done well, since one's attention is immediately drawn to her incorrect answer. One of the greatest challenges facing teachers of problem solving is to shift their focus away from what children *cannot* do and toward what children *can* do. Instead of pointing out children's errors and telling them how to fix their mistakes, we should focus on what children already know, then build on that knowledge.

Marisa attempted a solution for this problem and tried to record her thoughts in writing. These feats are significant accomplishments for a young child. Marisa has given her teacher a glimpse of her abilities. Although she had difficulty counting the tiles, she correctly modeled the first step in solving the problem.

## TIM'S WAY

> I used A cnocyaLATer I Pushed
> 25+25=50 and drowed A
> PiKitur ThATSHOW I Got
> The Answer 50 /ackages

I used a calculator. After I pushed 25 + 25 = 50
and drawed a picture that show(s)
I got the answer 50 packages.

Tim was the only child who attempted to use a traditional algorithm to solve this problem. When I asked him why he used addition, he replied, "Well, I gave each kid one card, and that's twenty-five, so do it again, and that's fifty." I asked Tim to show me the picture that he had made. He told me, "I drawed it in my head." When I asked him if he could show me what he had drawn in

his head, he replied, "No. I just see it." Finally, I asked Tim if he remembered how many cards were in each package. He said, "Five." At that point, Tim did not appear to realize that this information had anything to do with the problem. In his mind, this problem seemed to ask how many cards were needed. Since the cards came in packages, an answer of fifty packages made sense to him. Children frequently answer a different question than the one posed in the problem. This dissociation may represent a child's attempt to make sense of the original problem by transforming it into a simpler, more understandable form.

## BEN'S WAY

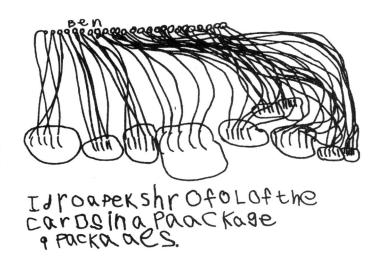

> I dropapeKshr OfoLOfthe
> carDsin a PaacKage
> 9 PacKa aes.

I drew a picture of all of the
cards in a package
9 packages.

Ben's solution is a good example of why we need to look at more than just a child's answer to a problem.

Although he solved the problem correctly—circling ten groups of five—he miscounted the number of groups, or packages.

Ben has shown a good understanding of the problem. His solution process reveals sound reasoning, and he provides a complete record of his work. I asked Ben why he did not label each part of his drawing to make it easier for others to understand. "I know what the circles and lines are," he replied. "Can't you figure it out?"

*(Continued on p. 40)*

## TAYLOR'S WAY

I dru 3 boxs and Figrd it wast enuf and I dru mor and cntd the srkls lik pepl til I had 25 kid and cntd the boxs 10 pakgs

Taylor January 19, 1994

I drew 3 boxes and I figured it wasn't enough and I drew more and counted the circles like people until I had 25 kid(s) and counted the boxes. 10 packages

Taylor's attempt to describe his solution process is typical of young children. Although he leaves out some details, we can use his drawing to fill in the blanks.

Taylor solved the problem in a logical and orderly manner and correctly used several mathematical terms (*enough, more,* and *counted*). Someday, he will learn that the strategy he employed is called "guess and check." For now, Taylor and his classmates call this strategy "Taylor's way."

## JAMIE'S WAY

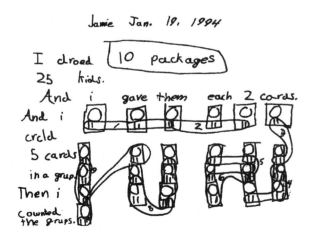

I droed 10 packages 25 kids. And i gave them each 2 cards. And i crcld 5 cards in a grup. Then i counted the grups.

I drew 10 packages 25 kids.
And I gave them each 2 cards. And I circled 5 cards in a group. Then I counted the groups.

Jamie's solution process is clear and complete. She has labeled some parts of her drawing and correctly used the mathematical terms *each, group,* and *counted.* Unlike those children who insist that their drawings look "real," Jamie is not afraid to use different shapes to designate each group.

## TRISTA'S WAY

5 10 2
10 20 4
15 30 6
20 40 8
25 50 10

I think it is hard cus i had so many kids. So i droo 5 kids and 2 cards in thr pokt not in thr hed like Bret thinks. I mad a lst so you can see 10 pkijs.

I think it is hard because I had so many kids. So I drew 5 kids and 2 cards in their pocket not in their head like Brett thinks. I made a list so you can see 10 packages.

Trista's organized list is quite impressive for a young child. When I asked why she did not label each column, she did not seem to understand my question. I then asked, "What are the numbers in the first column?"

"Oh," she said. "Those are the kids. Like if there was five of them, that's two packages. So you just keep going, ten kids, four packages; fifteen kids, six packages; and stuff like that."

When I asked how she used the drawing to the right of her list, she replied, "Well, that's how I knew five kids was two packages." Trista's sequential list represents a more sophisticated level of thinking than many of her classmates' solutions. Her ability to recognize the relationships within the list shows good number sense and an understanding of patterns.

## Angela's Way

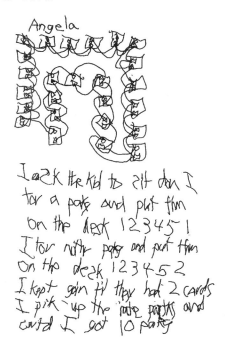

Angela

*I asked the kids to sit down. I tore a package and put them on the desks 1 2 3 4 5 1.*
*I tore another package and put them on the desks 1 2 3 4 5 2. I kept going until they had 2 cards. I picked up the empty packages and counted. I got 10 packages.*

I truly enjoyed watching Angela solve this problem. She took a deck of cards from the card tub, counted out five cards, wrapped them in a piece of paper, and glued the paper shut. She repeated this process four times. Next she walked to the front of the classroom and spoke to the children. "Please sit down so I can count you," she said. When the other children did not respond to her request, she asked me to repeat it.

After all the children were seated, Angela opened one package and placed two cards on the desk of the first child. Then she placed two cards on the desk of the second child. She placed the remaining card on the third child's desk, along with the paper wrapper. After opening a second package, she placed two cards on the desk of the fourth child. Several children immediately tried to tell Angela that she had given the third child only one card. She ignored their comments and continued to pass out cards as before. In this process, every third child received one card and a wrapper.

Realizing that she had not made enough packages, she went back to her desk and made four more. She again asked the children to sit down, then resumed passing out cards. Since she still did not have enough cards, she made four more packages. At this point, only one child had received no cards. Angela placed two

cards on this student's desk, and then she proceeded to give a second card to all the children who had previously received only one card. When she was finished, she walked around the room and gathered up the empty wrappers. She took the wrappers to her desk, counted them, and then announced to the class that the answer was "Ten wrappers."

Like Taylor, Angela demonstrated her own version of a traditional problem-solving strategy. The confidence she displayed by compelling the entire class to "act it out" is matched by her confidence in herself as a problem solver.

## Patrick's Way

Patrick

10 packages

*I drew 25 cards beneath each card I put 1 card under it.*
*But I put packages around them and I got the answer.*
*I put little boxes and then I counted by 2.*

After drawing five rows of ten cards each, Patrick solved the problem with a single stroke of his pen. The curving line in the center of his sketch neatly divides the cards into ten groups of five. I asked Patrick why he chose to make this particular drawing. "I don't know," he said. "It just looked good." As an adult, I can only marvel at the simplicity and elegance of his solution.

*(Continued on p. 42)*

## BRETT'S WAY

*i went 5 10 15 20 25 bukus*
*←es five in a patio*
*and pot 2 4 6 8 10 abuv it bukus*
*each porun git 2 and got*
*the ansr*

*2 4 6 8 10 10121408*
*5 10 15 20 25*

I went 5 10 15 20 25 because (it) has five in a package and put 2 4 6 8 10 above it because each person get(s) 2 and got the answer.

When I first looked at Brett's response, I did not understand his solution process. He seemed to have found the answer by coincidence, with the numbers in each row conveniently yielding the correct figure. Feeling puzzled, I initiated the following discussion:

*Mr. B.:* Tell me about how you solved this problem. How does your solution work?

*Brett:* I solved it this way because you get the answer.

*Mr. B.:* But why does your way of solving the problem get the answer?

*Brett:* Because the way I did it works.

*Mr. B.:* But how do you know it works?

*Brett:* Because you get the answer.

Defeated by Brett's circular logic, I was forced to decipher his solution by myself. He was right—it does work.

## SHARING SOLUTIONS IN THE "MATHEMATICIAN'S CHAIR"

Before starting "mathematician's chair," I gave four children (Ben, Jamie, Angela, and Patrick) blank overhead transparencies on which to record their solutions. In the discussion that follows, you will observe that I made many choices—deciding which statements to clarify, what topics to pursue, when to step back, and when to seize the teachable moment. As a teacher, I strive to remain flexible and adaptable, encouraging the activity to flow like a spirited conversation.

*Mr. B.:* Who solved the problem for the day? [Marisa volunteered to share her solution. Because I knew that it would take her some time to copy her drawing onto an overhead transparency, I asked the class a series of questions.] What do you think the circles and squares are in Marisa's drawing? What do these shapes represent?

*Whitney:* I think circles are kids, because that's their heads and squares are cards.

*Marisa:* You're right.

*Mr. B.:* How many circles and how many squares do you predict Marisa will draw?

*Curtis:* Twenty-five circles and twice that many squares.

*Mr. B.:* Curtis, what do you mean by "twice that many"?

*Curtis:* Fifty, because it's twenty-five once and then twenty-five twice. Like twenty-five, and you do it again. Like two times is twice.

*Mr. B.:* I would like everyone to write down what they think is twice as much of each of these numbers: 3, 5, 10, 12, 18, 20, 50, 75, and 100. If you don't know one of the answers, write what you think makes sense. When everyone is done, share your answers with someone sitting beside you. Also, tell your partner why you agree or disagree with her or his answers. [After the children finished recording and sharing their answers, I asked Curtis to lead the class in a discussion of the strategies they used to figure out each answer. By that time, Marisa had finished her drawing.]

*Marisa:* I drew the heads and cards, and I think it is fifty-nine packages. What's your questions and comments?

*Breanna:* I disagree because fifty-nine packages is way too much.

*Nick:* I agree with Breanna because each kid gets two cards, not two packages.

*Mr. B.:* Marisa, could you show the class how you solved the problem using the cubes and tiles that are on your desk?

Marisa walked to her desk and explained to the class how she had laid out twenty-five cubes to represent the children and two tiles under each cube to represent the cards. Joel asked her what she did next; Marisa replied that she counted the cards by twos. But when Marisa started to show the class how she had counted by twos, she stopped at ten, saying she couldn't count any farther. Since this problem can be solved without counting the cards, I asked Marisa why she felt that she needed to count them. She replied that it was necessary to find the answer. I then asked Marisa to count the cards by ones. She counted to twenty-eight, became confused, and started over. At that point, I asked one of the children to go with her to the back of the room and practice counting by ones and twos to fifty.

> *Mr. B.:* What could Marisa do so her solution will work?
>
> *Jamie:* She could put the cards in packages with circles or something.
>
> *Mr. B.:* Has anyone solved this problem in a different way? Tim, would you come up and share your solution?
>
> *Tim:* I used a calculator and did twenty-five and twenty-five is fifty packages. I wrote "25 + 25" for what I did. Comments and questions?
>
> *Gemma:* I agree because that is the way I did it and I got fifty packages too.
>
> *Curtis:* I disagree because that's how many cards, not how many packages.
>
> *Taylor:* I agree with Curtis because fifty packages would be way too many cards because there is five cards in a package. That would be a lot!
>
> *Mr. B.:* That is a very interesting problem. If there are five cards in each package, how many cards would be in fifty packages? When you think you know the answer, share how you figured it out with someone else.

Many of the children struggled to solve this new problem because it involved relatively large numbers. Although some were unable to determine a solution, all participated in the discussions. When the conversation stopped, I asked Tim what he thought the answer might be.

> *Tim:* It's a lot. Like, I think it is 250 cards. No, wait … I mean 255. No, wait … I mean 250.
>
> *Mr. B.:* How did you figure it out?
>
> *Tim:* Because I know one package is five, and you go 5, 5, 5, 5, 5, 5 and keep going until you get to 50 and then to a 100 and then 200 and then to 250.
>
> *Mr. B.:* But how do you know to stop at 250?

> *Tim:* You count by fives until you get to 50, and that's 10 fives. So another 10 [fives] is 100, and another 10 [fives] is 150, and another 10 [fives] is 200, and another 10 [fives] is 250, and that's 10, 10, 10, 10, 10 makes 50 fives, and 50 fives is 250.
>
> *Mr. B.:* Did anyone solve this new problem a different way?
>
> *Heather:* I just counted by fives on my fingers, and when I holded up fifty fingers, I stopped at 250.
>
> *Justin:* Five and five is ten, and I know there is 10 tens in 100. So there's 20 tens in 200 and 25 tens in 250. So you count by tens, and it's 250 because there are twice as many fives as tens. [At this point, I chose to return to the original problem.]
>
> *Mr. B.:* Tim, if fifty packages is the same as 250 cards, how many packages is the same as fifty cards? [Faced with this question, Tim experienced what I call "deer in the headlights syndrome," or what some brain researchers call "downshifting" (Caine and Caine 1991). An expression of panic swept over Tim's face, and he was unable to see the next step in the solution process.]
>
> *Justin:* Tim, if you had ten cards, how many packages would you get?
>
> *Tim:* That's easy. Two, because five and five is ten.
>
> *Justin:* So how many packages is 15 cards?
>
> *Tim:* I don't get it.
>
> *Mr. B.:* Justin, would you like to go with Tim to the back carpet and show him the pattern that you are using: ten cards, fifteen cards, twenty cards, twenty-five cards, and so on?

When children "downshift" during mathematician's chair, teachers have several alternatives: ask leading questions, ask children to return to their seats and think about the problem, or ask children to discuss the problem with someone in a more private setting. Once children have downshifted, they often have a great deal of difficulty relaxing and listening to ideas that contradict their current ways of thinking.

> *Mr. B.:* Does someone else have a different solution? Ben, would you share next?
>
> *Ben:* I think it is nine packages because I counted the circles and got nine. Questions or comments?

*Breanna:* I agree and disagree, because I kind of agree because you drew the kids and the packages. But I disagree because you should count the circles again. [As Ben counted the circles at the top of his paper, a confused look came over his face.] I mean the circles at the bottom of your paper. [Ben counted the circles at the bottom of his paper.]

*Ben:* It's ten packages, not nine. [He gave the class a big smile.]

*Mr. B.:* Why do you think Ben drew twenty-five little circles at the top of his paper?

*Angela:* Those are the kids in the room.

*Mr. B.:* What are the lines at the bottom of Ben's drawing?

*Gemma:* The cards.

*Mr. B.:* Ben, what are the long lines between the kids and the cards?

*Ben:* Those show who gets the cards.

*Mr. B.:* Are there any more questions or comments for Ben?

*Angela:* I think Ben draws good.

*Mr. B.:* Has anyone solved the problem in a way that is different from what has been shared so far? Taylor, would you share next? [Taylor drew his solution on an overhead transparency.]

*Taylor:* I drew three boxes and put cards in them for the kids that are the circles, but that wasn't enough. So I kept on drawing circles and lines inside the boxes until I had twenty-five kids. Then I counted the boxes and got ten boxes. Questions or comments?

*Trista:* I agree because he put five cards in each one [package] and some kids get a card from two of them, so it works.

*Joel:* I agree. Taylor did it like me, and I got ten packages.

*Trista:* But why did you draw just three boxes?

*Taylor:* Because I didn't know how many there was, so I just kept drawing and counting until I had enough. Are the questions done?

*Mr. B.:* I think you have all done some great problem solving this morning. Let's take a break so we can relax and refocus.

We continued the activity after recess.

*Mr. B.:* Who has a different solution? Jamie, would you share your solution?

*Jamie:* My way is kind of like Taylor's, but I numbered the packages so I don't need to count them.

*Ben:* I agree because she gots ten packages like me.

*Taylor:* I agree because she gave each kid two cards and she put five cards in each package like the problem says.

*Joel:* I agree with Taylor and Ben because she did it the right way.

*Mr. B.:* Joel, what do you mean "the right way"?

*Joel:* She drew the kids and the cards and the packages the right way.

*Mr. B.:* Joel, how do you think Jamie knew how many kids and cards to draw?

*Joel:* She looked at how many it said there were in the problem.

*Mr. B.:* Joel, so how did she know how many packages to draw?

*Joel:* Well, when she had twenty-five kids, she had enough.

*Mr. B.:* Are there any more questions or comments for Jamie? Who solved this problem a different way? Trista, would you share your solution next?

*Trista:* It's like a pattern, because five kids is two packages, ten kids is four packages, and it just keeps going like that. Comments or questions?

*Matthew:* I don't get it, because five kids is ten, not two.

*Mr. B.:* Matthew, what do you mean, it is "ten, not two"?

*Matthew:* I mean, five kids is ten cards, not two cards like Trista said.

*Trista:* Matt, it's two packages, not ten packages.

*Matthew:* I still don't get it.

*Mr. B.:* Trista, how many cards would you need for five children?

*Trista:* Ten cards because you can see them in their pockets right here. [Trista points to the overhead transparency and counts the cards on each side of the people she has drawn.]

*Matthew:* I still don't get it.

*Mr. B.:* Trista, could you write some labels at the top of each of the columns in your list?

[Trista wrote "kids" above the left-hand column, "cards" above the middle column, and "packages" above the remaining column.]

Trista: Matt, do you get it?

Matthew: Yes, but I still don't get why you counted by fives in the kids row.

Trista: I just used five because it made it easy. Like if you put six or something the packages won't come out. Like you'd get a fraction like two and one-fourth or something like that. No, it's two and two out of five, but I don't know how to say it.

Mr. B.: If you did put six children in the kids column, what would go in the packages column?

Patrick: Trista's right. It's two and two-fifths. [At this point, a teacher might begin a discussion of fractions. Or you might save this discussion for a warm-up activity on the following day.]

Mr. B.: What if you put thirty in the kids column, what would go in the packages column? Whisper to your neighbor when both of you think you know the answer.

Gemma: It's easy. It's twelve because the kids is counting [by] fives and the packages is counting [by] twos.

Mr. B.: What if you put a fifty in the kids column, what would go in the packages column?

Tim: Twenty because it's twenty-five [kids] twice, so it's ten [packages] twice.

Whitney: I agree because if you count thirty, thirty-five, forty, forty-five, fifty, that's five more, so it's twelve, fourteen, sixteen, eighteen, twenty.

Trista: I agree because twenty-five is half of fifty, so ten is half of twenty. So just go bigger instead of littler.

Mr. B.: Are there any more questions or comments for Trista? Does anyone else have a different solution? Angela, will you share next?

Angela: I counted the wrappers and it was ten wrappers. Questions and comments?

Jamie: I agree because she put the cards on our desks and we each got two.

Marisa: I agree because she did it real good.

Mr. B.: It was easy to see what Angela did, since we all watched her pass out the cards. Are there any more questions for Angela?

Justin: Why did you give some kids one card?

Angela: Because the wrapper was empty. So I got another one and gave them two from some more.

Mr. B.: Does anyone else have a question or comment for Angela? Are there any other different solutions? Patrick, would you go next?

Patrick: I drew twenty-five cards, and I put another card under each one, and I drew the packages and counted them by twos.

Heather: Where did you draw the kids?

Patrick: I didn't, because I just drew the cards instead and I knew it was twenty-five and twenty-five.

Taylor: Why didn't you put the packages in a line like me?

Patrick: I don't know. It just looked good.

Mr. B.: Why did you count by twos?

Patrick: Because there are two packages in each row that is cut in half.

Mr. B.: Are there any more questions or comments for Patrick? Who solved the problem a different way? Brett, would you share your solution to this problem?

Brett: It's counting by fives because there is five in a package, and it's counting by twos on top because they each get two. So it's ten packages.

Trista: I agree because Brett kind of did it like me, only he laid them on their side.

Mr. B.: Trista, what do you mean when you say "he laid them on their side"?

Trista: The rows go across instead of up and down like mine.

Mr. B.: Does anyone know what people call a list when it goes up and down?

Breanna: I think it's a tall row.

Joel: I think it's a column.

Mr. B.: I agree with Joel. It's called a column, and when the list goes across the paper, it's called a row. Brett, I'm confused because if the bottom row is cards, then ten cards should be two packages, not four packages.

Brett: But each kid gets two cards, so it's four not two.

Mr. B.: I still don't understand.

*Matthew:* See, it's not five cards—it's five cards in a package, like Brett said. So if they get one card, it would be one package. But they get two cards, so that's two packages.

*Mr. B.:* I wonder if Brett's way would work if we changed some of the numbers in the problem. What if there were fifteen kids and they each get three cards? Would Brett's way work? When you have solved this problem, share your solution with your neighbor.

*Brett:* It still works because it's nine packages just like I thought.

*Audrey:* Brett's right. It really works.

*Mr. B.:* For your homework tonight, I would like you to try some other problems with different numbers and see if Brett's way will always work. If you don't understand Brett's way, solve the problems in a way that makes sense to you. Are there any questions or comments?

*Jamie:* How many cards should we use?

*Mr. B.:* As many as you want.

*Ben:* How many kids are there?

*Mr. B.:* As many as you want. You decide how many children, how many cards are in a package, and how many cards each person gets.

*Marisa:* Do we have to find the answer?

*Mr. B.:* Yes, and be sure to show how you solved each problem. Those were good questions, Marisa, Ben, and Jamie. Are there any more questions or comments? All of you are super problem solvers. I can't wait to see your problems and solutions when you bring them to school tomorrow. Now let's compare some of the solutions that were shared today. How were they alike?

*Trista:* Brett kind of solved it like me, only the rows went across not up and down.

*Breanna:* Jamie and Ben drew the kids and the cards and circled the packages.

*Curtis:* Tim did twenty-five and twenty-five like Patrick, only he used a calculator.

*Gemma:* They all are kind of alike because they didn't name the things they drew, but we could figure it out anyway.

*Mr. B.:* How were some of the solutions different?

*Joel:* Angela was real different. She made us sit down, and she passed them out.

*Mr. B.:* Why was Angela's solution easy to understand?

*Whitney:* Because we watched her pass them out and count the wrappers.

*Nick:* She passed them out, and everyone watched her so we know what she did.

*Audrey:* I think Taylor was different because he drew the boxes first instead of the kids and the cards like everyone else.

*Whitney:* I think Tim was different because he used a calculator.

*Mr. B.:* How did the calculator help Tim solve the problem?

*Patrick:* Well, it didn't really, because he didn't get the answer. He did good when he did twenty-five plus twenty-five is fifty, but he only got the cards not the packages.

*Mr. B.:* How could Tim use the calculator to get the packages?

*Heather:* Well, I think he should have done fifty divide [by] five, but I'm not sure.

*Mr. B.:* Tim, would you try Heather's way on your calculator and see what happens?

*Tim:* It's ten.

*Matthew:* Heather's way will work, but you can do it easier. Just keep pushing fives until you get fifty, and then count how many fives there was.

*Mr. B.:* Tim, why don't you try Matthew's way and see what you get?

*Tim:* It's ten again.

*Mr. B.:* How did Taylor's and Jamie's drawings help them solve the problem?

*Audrey:* They could see the cards inside the packages, and so they didn't get messed up when they counted them.

*Curtis:* It made it easy to find the answer because you could just see what it was.

*Mr. B.:* Were there any solutions that were hard to understand?

*Curtis:* Trista's was kind of hard until she told us what the numbers were.

*Mr. B.:* Are there any more questions or comments about today's problem or the solutions that were shared?

*Marisa:* Mr. B., when are you going to buy the cards and give them to us?

## QUESTIONS AND ANSWERS ABOUT MATHEMATICIAN'S CHAIR

### What is the teacher's role during mathematician's chair?

As teacher, my primary role is to learn from the children in the mathematician's chair. I try to do whatever is needed to understand children's thinking and to help the rest of the class understand as well. I ask probing questions, especially if the solution contains an error that the other children do not see. However, I try to reserve my comments or questions until the children are finished. Intervening too soon can limit further discussion by the children and rob them of the opportunity to discover errors for themselves. When children are in the mathematician's chair, teachers should—

- encourage children to give reasons for why they agree or disagree with one another;
- focus the discussion on solution processes rather than the answer alone;
- use children's solutions as a springboard to reinforce or teach new skills;
- ask probing questions to see whether children are confident in their solution strategies and whether they can explain their solutions clearly and completely;
- model active listening (see fig. 5.1); and
- recognize risk-taking and show that they value mistakes as learning opportunities.

During mathematician's chair, "teachers must build a community in which students will feel free to express their ideas. [Additionally,] students in the lower grades need help from teachers in order to share mathematical ideas with one another in ways that are clear enough for other students to understand" (NCTM, 2000, p. 61).

---

Fig. 5.1. Guidelines for active listeners

- I can keep my eyes on the speaker.
- I can restate what the speaker has said in my own words.
- I can comment on what the speaker has said or ask questions of the speaker.
- I can visualize and predict what the speaker might say or do next.

---

### Why do children share their solutions with another child before sharing in mathematician's chair?

Most young children need a chance to try out their ideas on at least one other person before they share their thoughts with the entire class. Sharing with another person has the following benefits:

- Children sometimes notice mistakes in their calculations or errors in their logic.
- Children practice and develop communication and social skills in a semiprivate setting.
- Children see their partner's solution and can compare it with their own.

When children engage in respectful conversations, both speaker and listener benefit. When speaking, children organize and clarify their thinking as they attempt to put their thoughts into words. When listening, children have the opportunity to examine and reflect on the ideas of others. The process of sharing ideas extends and expands the understanding of all participants.

Talking with peers in cooperative learning groups is especially important for young children. Children become comfortable with new words when they are free to experiment with them in a nonthreatening environment. If a word has not been incorporated in a child's listening or speaking vocabulary, it is not likely to exist in her or his functional reading and writing vocabularies. Children will communicate more fluently in the language of mathematics when we give them frequent opportunities to hear and speak mathematics with others. "Language is as important to learning mathematics as it is to learning to read" (NCTM 2000, p. 128). Teachers should encourage children to talk about mathematics, share their ideas, and compare their strategies.

### What if children are unwilling to share their solutions with the class?

This concern is often expressed by teachers who have never used the mathematician's-chair approach. In practice, the opposite is usually true—every child wants to share her or his solution, even when it closely resembles a previous response.

If you are confronted with unwilling participants, however, here are some useful strategies:

- Give children a chance to share their solutions with at least one other person before asking them to share with the class.
- Compliment children on their solutions while they

are working on them, and ask students if they would be willing to share in the mathematician's chair.

- Ask children to share their solutions from their desks while you record their drawings or explanations on an overhead transparency or chalkboard.
- Give children a problem with multiple answers. After they solve the problem, ask children to raise their hands if they found a specific answer, and then select a participant from this group.

## Why do children agree or disagree rather than determine who is right or wrong?

This practice was inspired by the children themselves, after several expressed a dislike for being told they were "wrong." We decided to begin our comments with either "I agree because . . ." or "I disagree because . . . ."

As I considered the reasons that children did not want their peers to use the word *wrong*, I realized that this term tended to shift attention from the solution process to the solution's author. The statement "You're wrong," implies that a person is wrong, not an answer or solution process. The words *agree* and *disagree* seem to be more emotionally neutral terms. In any event, the words *right* and *wrong* seem inappropriate for situations in which a correct solution process can yield a faulty answer, or vice versa. Using the phrases "I agree because . . ." or "I disagree because . . ." forces children to think more deeply about their claims.

> When children are involved in discussions in which they justify solutions—especially in the face of disagreement—[they] will gain better mathematical understanding as they work to convince their peers about differing points of view. It is important that students understand that the focus is not on who is right or wrong but rather on whether an answer makes sense and can be justified (NCTM 2000, pp. 60, 198).

## Why do children applaud during mathematician's chair?

This practice also was initiated by the children. We had used the mathematician's-chair idea for several years without applauding. One day, a child shared a solution that appealed to several of her peers. When she started to return to her desk, a few children began to applaud. The other children and I joined in. Since that time, it has become a part of our classroom culture.

Even if the children had not suggested this practice, I should have introduced it. A round of applause demonstrates courtesy and respect for the speaker. It recognizes the effort that children have exhibited in solving the problem, and it commends their willingness to share their thinking with others. It also sends a message to children that their ideas are valued and appreciated by others.

I encourage other teachers to consider this practice. However, like all aspects of the share-and-compare model, it can be modified or omitted. I do not suggest that this book describes the only way to teach problem solving. I simply wish to share a model that I and others have used with success in our classrooms.

## What if a child shares a solution that is incorrect or contains an error?

Children should learn to see mistakes as learning opportunities. In fact, mistakes often lead to the most interesting discussions during mathematician's chair. They also provide a rich source of ideas for additional problems.

## What if children are rude or inattentive during mathematician's chair?

Many teachers have found that "by approaching traditional [mathematics] topics in ways that emphasize conceptual understanding and problem solving, many apparently uninterested students can become quite engaged" (NCTM 2000, p. 372). Before the children solve their first mathematics problem, however, I share two expectations with them. First, we should be responsible for ourselves. Second, we should be respectful of others.

## Do consequences result if these expectations are not met?

Individual classroom teachers should determine the consequences for any rude behaviors, according to their own discipline programs. In my experience, the teacher sets the tone for classroom discourse. Children will not value one another's ideas until the teacher values the ideas of each child.

> Students are more likely to develop confidence and self-assurance as problem solvers in classrooms where . . . everyone's ideas are respected and valued. These attitudes are essential if students are expected to make sense of mathematics and to take intellectual risks by asking questions, formulating conjectures, and offering mathematical argument (NCTM 2000, p. 185).

## Do you recommend that children use an overhead projector instead of the chalkboard to display their solutions?

Our use of the overhead projector was another of the many ideas suggested by the children. Both overhead projectors and chalkboards have their advantages. We prefer an overhead projector for the following reasons:

- Children's handwriting is often more legible on an overhead transparency, since it more closely resembles a sheet of paper. When writing on a chalkboard, some children have difficulty making their letters large enough to read.
- Children can face their audience while they write or sketch, allowing a dialogue to occur. When using the chalkboard, children must turn their backs to the audience.
- Children can prepare overhead transparencies before their turns in the mathematician's chair. This practice promotes a more efficient use of classroom time.

However, the chalkboard may be preferable to the overhead projector when comparing solutions, as several responses can be displayed simultaneously.

## How do you maintain classroom interest when a child requires extra time to record a solution?

Such delays can create difficulties in classroom management. I use several different techniques to cope with these circumstances:

- As mentioned above, I often ask children with especially detailed solutions to copy their responses to overhead transparencies before their turns in the mathematician's chair.
- On other occasions, I engage the rest of the class in a series of questions. For example, I might ask, "What do you think she is doing? Why do you think she is doing it that way? What do you think she will do next? Do you notice anything missing from this solution?"
- I also encourage children to speak while they write or sketch—to tell the audience what they are doing while they are doing it.
- When two children have similar solutions, or have solved the problem as a team, both can "sit" in the

mathematician's chair. They can then share the duties of presenting their solution; one can draw while the other talks.

- When appropriate, I may present children's solutions for them. This practice gives me the opportunity to model the sharing process.
- If lack of time becomes an even more pressing issue, you can ask children to work on large sheets of chart paper. These sheets can then be displayed during mathematician's chair, eliminating the need for copying to a chalkboard or transparency.
- You may wish to divide the class into smaller groups for sharing their solutions, assigning each group to a different part of the classroom. This format gives each child more time to speak but reduces the number and variety of solutions to which each is exposed.

## Do you ever share your solution to the problem?

In general, I do not share my way of solving the problem. I prefer to focus on the children's solutions. By sharing my solution process, I risk two disagreeable consequences. First, some children may place less value on their own or their classmates' solutions. Second, some children may unthinkingly apply my strategy to other problems rather than try to solve problems in ways that make sense to them. On rare occasions, however, I do make exceptions. For example, if a problem seems to lend itself to a particular strategy, and none of the children use that approach, I might model that strategy.

## When the teacher does not model new or more mature ways of thinking, doesn't that limit children's learning?

I do not propose that teachers refrain from modeling new or more mature ways of solving problems. However, I prefer to suggest new strategies by methods other than direct instruction. For example, I might solve a problem written by a child, then ask all the children each to write me a letter explaining why he or she agrees or disagrees with my solution. I also may attribute a solution to a fictitious character, then use a series of questions to elicit the children's responses.

## What do you do when children share similar solutions even though the teacher has asked for different solutions?

This predicament is almost certain to occur with young children. If one child uses line segments to represent birds, whereas another child uses circles, many children will say that the two solutions are different. In this situation, I try to be patient. After mathematician's chair, when children are comparing solutions, I try to help them see how some aspects of their solutions are mathematically similar and others are significantly different.

## When children compare solutions, what kinds of things should they discuss?

I try to keep the discussion focused on "what makes sense" in the solutions. I try to avoid discussion of which solutions are better or worse. In my role as facilitator, I ask the following questions:

- Why does this solution make sense?
- Why is this solution easy or hard to understand?
- How does this solution help you solve this or other problems?

# 6 ASSESSING WHAT CHILDREN SHARE AND COMPARE

We must ensure that tests measure what is of value, not just what is easy to test. If we want students to investigate, explore and discover, assessment must not measure just mimicry mathematics. By confusing means and ends, by making testing more important than learning, present practice holds today's students hostage to yesterday's mistakes.

—National Research Council, *Everybody Counts*

When assessment is an integral part of mathematics instruction, it contributes significantly to all students' mathematics learning.

—National Council of Teachers of Mathematics, *Principles and Standards for School Mathematics*

Most people are familiar with this Chinese proverb:

> I hear and I forget.
>
> I see and I remember.
>
> I do and I understand.

However, I do not think the proverb is quite complete. I would like to add one more line:

> I hear and I forget.
>
> I see and I remember.
>
> I do and I understand.
>
> I reflect and I improve.

Children become better problem solvers primarily through reflection, not memorization. Their skills improve as they consider—

- past experiences and previous knowledge;
- ways to communicate solutions orally and in writing;
- comments or questions about their solutions;
- mistakes and corrections;
- solutions proposed by others; and
- comparisons of different solutions.

"Through the use of good tasks and the public discussion of criteria for good responses, teachers can cultivate in their students both the disposition and the capacity to engage in self-assessment and reflection on their own work and on ideas put forth by others" (NCTM 2000, p. 22). The share-and-compare model aims to develop not only the ability to solve problems but also the capacity to assess one's own performance.

Just as the traditional drill-and-practice approach has its limitations for teaching problem solving, traditional types of evaluation have their limitations for assessing problem-solving skills and abilities. Such instruments typically do not—

- describe how children learn to think mathematically;
- explain why children make errors; or
- suggest how children can improve as problem solvers.

As noted in *Principles and Standards for School Mathematics* (NCTM 2000, p. 23),

> [o]verreliance on [tests] may give an incomplete and perhaps distorted picture of students' performance. To maximize the instructional value of assessment, teachers need to move beyond a superficial 'right or wrong' analysis of tasks to a focus on how students are thinking about the tasks. Efforts should be made to identify valuable student insights on which further progress can be based rather than to concentrate solely on errors or misconceptions. Although less straightforward than averaging scores on quizzes, assembling evidence from a variety of sources is more likely to yield an accurate picture of what each student knows and is able to do.

The alternative forms of assessment described in this chapter include direct observation, interviews, rubrics, and portfolios. These tools complement the share-and-compare model, provide children with useful feedback, and furnish teachers with valuable diagnostic information. For a more complete description of alternative assessment practices, you may wish to consult the following sources:

- *Assessing Reasoning and Problem Solving: A Sourcebook for Elementary School Teachers* (Krulick and Rudnick 1998)
- *Emphasis on Assessment: Readings from NCTM's School-Based Journals* (Lambdin, Kehle, and Preston 1996)
- *Assessment Standards for School Mathematics* (NCTM 1995)
- *Assessment in the Mathematics Classroom* (Webb 1993)
- *Measure for Measure: Using Portfolios in K–8 Mathematics* (Kuhs 1997)
- *Finding the Connections: Linking Assessment, Instruction, and Curriculum in Elementary Mathematics* (Moon and Schulman 1995)

## DIRECT OBSERVATION

Teachers observe children all day, but they do not always record their observations for the purposes of assessment. Since spoken and written solutions do not always reveal a complete or accurate picture of a child's level of understanding, ongoing assessment is a useful tool. I admit that simultaneously supervising children, facilitating learning, and conducting student observations can be difficult. Considering the natural restrictions on a teacher's time and endurance, here are some suggestions for making classroom observation more manageable:

- Limit the number of children you observe each day.
- Limit the time you observe each child.
- Use a checklist of specific behaviors that you wish to observe (fig. 6.1).
- Write observations on index cards or sticky notes so that they can be attached to student portfolios or records.
- Carry writing materials with you at all times.

---

Fig. 6.1. A checklist of specific behaviors

When observing children solving problems, try to answer these questions:

- What type of manipulative or other tool do children use, and how do they use it?
- Do children display problem-solving dispositions (patience, perseverance, positive attitude, flexibility, and fluency)?
- Do children take risks, such as working alone or using an unfamiliar manipulative?
- Do children ask questions of others, and what kinds of questions do they ask?
- Do children constantly monitor their solution process while working on a problem, and can they justify their solution when they are finished?
- Do children work collaboratively with others?

When observing children discussing solutions in Mathematician's Chair, try to answer these questions:

- Do children present their solution in a way that others can understand?
- Do children present their solution process clearly and completely?
- Do children see their errors, and are they able to correct them?
- Do children agree or disagree with the person in the mathematician's chair, and tell why?
- Do children ask meaningful questions of the person in the mathematician's chair?
- Do children listen respectfully to the person in the mathematician's chair?

# INTERVIEWS

"Because students learn by connecting new ideas to prior knowledge, teachers must understand what their students already know" (NCTM 2000, p. 18). An interview can be a useful tool for gaining this understanding. Guidelines for conducting an interview are presented in figure 6.2. Before conducting an interview, I give the child a challenging problem, then record what the child says and does during the solution process. Examples of prompts to elicit the child's thinking are given in figure 6.3. When the child has finished solving the problem, I ask questions (fig. 6.4) that are designed to determine the child's knowledge and comprehension of the mathematics involved, ability to successfully explain the solution process, and ability to recognize errors and learn from mistakes.

---

**Fig. 6.2. Guidelines for conducting an interview**

- Try to insure that you and the child will not be interrupted and that distractions are minimized.

- Have available a broad range of tools for the child to use (manipulatives, rulers, graph paper, Judy clocks, play money, calculators, and so on).

- Pose a problem that will truly challenge the child.

- Remind the child to solve the problem in a way that makes sense. Focus on the child's solution process, not on the misuse of mathematical terms or errors in computation. Extending or expanding a child's thinking is very difficult until you first determine how a child approaches a problem. However, most children think very differently than adults, so seeing the problem from a child's point of view can be very challenging.

- When asking questions, start with very open-ended questions (fig. 6.3), then proceed to more specific questions as you gain insight into the reasons behind the child's thinking (fig. 6.4).

- Record what the child actually says and does, not what you expect to hear and see.

---

**Fig. 6.3. Open-ended questions for the beginning of an interview**

That is very interesting. Can you tell me what you did?

Please show me what you did and tell me about it.

How did you find the answer?

How did you figure the problem out?

Please tell me more about what you did, so I can understand you better.

I never thought about it that way. Can you tell me more?

---

**Fig. 6.4. Specific questions to be used later in an interview**

Why did you do that?

How did you check your answer to see if it is correct?

Why did you say that?

Explain your drawing to me.

What do these lines mean?

What did you think in your head when you were doing this part of the problem?

How did you find the answer so quickly?

What do you mean when you say it is more?

Why did you use a number sentence for this part of the problem?

---

For more information about student interviews, the reader may wish to review "Using Student Interviews to Guide Classroom Instruction: An Action Research Project," by Larry Buschman (*Teaching Children Mathematics 8* [December 2001]:222–27).

# RUBRICS

Rubrics come in a wide variety of shapes and sizes. However, all rubrics share two features. First, they describe criteria for evaluation. In other words, they tell both teachers and students what qualities are important in students' solutions to problems. Second, they define levels of achievement.

Figure 6.5 shows a relatively simple holistic rubric. Figure 6.6 is an adaptation of a more complicated analytic rubric published by the Oregon Department of Education. Appendix 6 includes a selection of actual student solutions, scored using a modified version of the Oregon scoring guide (rubric).

---

**Fig. 6.5. A holistic scoring guide (rubric) for problem solving in mathematics**

**High:** The solution is complete, and the answer is correct. The child communicates the solution process clearly and effectively and demonstrates understanding of the concepts and skills necessary for solving the problem.

**Medium:** The solution is complete but may contain errors in logic or computation. The child communicates the solution process and appears to have at least a partial understanding of the concepts and skills necessary for solving the problem.

**Low:** The solution is incomplete, and the answer is incorrect. The child's communication of the solution process is unclear and ineffective. The child appears to have little understanding of the concepts and skills necessary for solving the problem.

---

Fig. 6.6. Analytic scoring guide (rubric)

**Young Reader's Mathematics Scoring Guide 2000–2001**

| | Conceptual Understanding | Process and Strategies | Verification | Communication |
|---|---|---|---|---|
| | Interpreting the concepts of the task and translating them into mathematics. | Choosing strategies that can work, then carrying out the strategies. | In addition to solving the task, identifiable evidence of a second look at the concepts/strategies/calculations to defend a solution. | Using pictures, symbols, and/or vocabulary to convey the path to the identifiable solution. |
| | **What?** | **How?** | **Check!** | **Show!** |
| **6** | The problem is changed into complete ideas that work *and* is connected to other math ideas. | A complete plan with several steps is used to solve the problem. | A new way may be used for solving the problem a second time to check the first answer. | The path through the work is very clear, showing every idea and step. |
| **5** | The problem is changed into complete math ideas that work. | A complete plan using pictures, charts, words, graphs, or numbers is used to solve the problem. | The second time solving the problem is clear and complete, checking all parts of the work. | The path through all parts of the work to the answer is shown. |
| **4** | The problem is changed into math ideas that can work. | A plan using pictures, charts, words, graphs, or numbers is used to solve the problem. | The problem is solved a second time, checking ideas, math steps, and the answer. | The path through the work to the answer is shown. |
| **3** | Parts of the problem are changed into math ideas that can work. | The plan could solve some parts of the problem, *or* the plan has a few missing parts. | Some but not all of the work is checked. | The path is not clear *or* doesn't show much of the work. |
| **2** | Only a little of the problem is understood, or the problem is changed into some ideas that do not work. | The plan has many missing parts *or* has some parts that cannot work. | Only a part of the work is checked. | The path is just started *or is* not shown at all. |
| **1** | Only a very small part of the problem is understood *or* no ideas are shown. | The plan cannot work, the plan is just started, *or* no work is shown. | The check does not work, is just started, *or* is not shown. | The path connecting concepts, strategies, and/or verification toward a solution is ineffective, minimal, or not evident. |

**Accuracy: Is the answer correct?**

| (5) The answer is correct, and the work shows steps that can get it. | (4) The work had a small mistake, but the important parts of the work are fine. | | (1) The answer is not correct, not finished, or does not match the work. |
|---|---|---|---|

Adapted from Oregon Department of Education, Office of Assessment and Evaluation, July 2000

---

Children can use rubrics to evaluate their own work or to revise and improve an assignment. They can even develop their own rubrics as shown in figures 6.7 and 6.8. When children construct their own rubrics, they should ask themselves the following questions:

- What makes my work good?
- How can I make it better?
- Does my work make sense?
- How can I make it easier for someone else to understand?

For their initial attempts, you may wish to encourage children to use criteria that can be answered with simple responses, such as "yes," "no," or "not yet." You also may wish to limit this initial scoring to one or two traits. When discussing solutions, try to use the language of the rubric in your comments. Instead of saying, "Good job," for example, you might say, "I like the way you used a drawing, because it makes it easier for me to understand what you have done."

I also recommend combining the use of rubrics with portfolios, since the two approaches complement each other:

- Rubrics help children decide what to include in their portfolio, and they help teachers assess a portfolio's contents.
- Rubrics help children with goal setting, which is part of the portfolio process.
- Portfolios document children's progress and growth toward meeting the standards of achievement described by the rubric.

---

Fig. 6.7. Student-created rubric for mathemetics problem solving (first grade)

1—No good

2—Need to try harder

3—OK

4—Good

5—Real Nice

---

Fig. 6.8. Student-created rubric for mathemetics problem solving (second grade)

Got the answer
   5—Got all the answers.
   3—Got some of the answers.
   1—Got only one answer.

Writing
   5—We all can read it.
   3—They can read it the next day.
   1—They can't read it.

Show and Tell
   5—Show and tell.
   3—They showed but didn't tell.
   1—They didn't show and tell.

---

I should mention here that providing young children with lists of criteria organized in a rubric does not ensure that they will understand those criteria or how to apply them. The criteria that children use to judge the quality of their work may differ significantly from the criteria used by adults. Therefore, teachers should not be surprised when children do not immediately use the feedback that they receive from rubrics to change their problem-solving behaviors. Although rubrics have a place in the problem-solving classroom, they must be used within a larger context of activities. In my experience, children learn best when they receive routine opportunities to—

- share their work with others;
- compare their work with that of others;
- observe role models who demonstrate the abilities, characteristics, and behaviors that accompany successful completion of complex tasks;
- examine solutions that demonstrate excellence in problem solving;
- engage in self-assessment;
- use multiple assessment tools to examine their performance from several different perspectives; and
- revise their work.

# PORTFOLIOS

Although teachers and children should use many types of assessment in a problem-solving classroom, the maintenance of a student portfolio is perhaps the most important. The portfolio becomes the focal point of assessment efforts because it provides each child with—

- a task that mirrors a real-world activity;
- a context in which to practice reflection and self-assessment; and
- a process for gaining systematic feedback on performance and progress.

In addition to these benefits, each portfolio provides the teacher with—

- a detailed picture of the child's academic skills;
- a history of the child's mathematical development;
- examples of work that highlight and celebrate the unique talents of each child; and
- a summary of each child's work that can be used to enrich and improve parent conferences.

Because the portfolio's primary purpose is to engage children in the process of ongoing self-assessment, children should create and maintain their own portfolios, with the guidance and assistance of their teacher. By performing this task themselves, children learn to—

- share their current level of performance with others;
- compare current and past levels of performance;
- observe changes in performance and consider the reasons for such changes; and
- set goals for improvement.

I have discussed the use of portfolios in other publications (Buschman 1993) but offer the following suggestions here.

*Start small, and emphasize quality, not quantity.* If your curriculum is organized around subject areas, start portfolios with work samples from mathematics only. If you use an integrated or thematic curriculum, begin with samples from one unit.

*Be realistic.* Portfolios are not the answer to all assessment needs; they can be misused just as any other tool for evaluation can.

*Although children should select most items for inclusion in their portfolios, you may want to select some items.* You can discriminate between items selected by students and those chosen by teachers by marking work samples with the letter S or T, for example.

*Ask children to date all items placed in their portfolios.* You can post a calendar in a prominent place or purchase date stamps for children to use.

*Make portfolios accessible to children.* Children can store their work in hanging files, large manila folders, or plastic milk crates.

*Maintain a table of contents for each portfolio.* This practice is especially important when certain items—such as audiotapes, videotapes, and computer disks—are not stored in the portfolio itself.

*Provide opportunities for parents to review portfolios with children.* Since some parents may be unfamiliar with the use of portfolios, they may not immediately recognize the value of these tools. A sequence of regularly scheduled portfolio conferences, led by the child, will persuade parents to appreciate portfolios' merits.

A portfolio should be more than a collection of papers. If you already use portfolios in the classroom, you may wish to experiment with some enhancements. For example, you can add audio or video recordings of a child's performance in the mathematician's chair. As I mentioned in the previous section, children can use rubrics to help select items for their portfolios or to revise items already stored there.

---

Fig. 6.9. Typical portfolio requests

- What is something from your portfolio that shows you can add any two numbers between 0 and 100?

- What is something from your portfolio that shows you know the names of the pattern blocks?

- Use one sample from your portfolio that shows you are persistent.

- What is something from your portfolio that shows you can find more than one answer to a problem?

- Show me something from your portfolio in which you solved a problem that asked you to find the perimeter.

- Show me something from your portfolio in which you did a survey and graphed your results. Tell me what I can learn from your graph.

- Show me a problem that you have written that was solved by at least three other people.

- Show me a problem from your portfolio that you solved using a calculator, and tell me why you used a calculator for this problem but not for others.

- From your portfolio, show me 10 problems in which you checked to see if your answer was correct.

The portfolio can become an important tool for learning. In my classroom, students participate in routine portfolio conferences. I divide these conferences into two parts. During the first part of the conference, the child examines the portfolio's contents, removes any items that he or she considers outdated, and then reviews the portfolio's organization. (Note: Some young children may be far too eager to remove items. Since one of the portfolio's purposes is to track improvement over time, you may wish to caution children not to remove items prematurely.)

After this initial stage of the conference, I give the child two or three "portfolio requests" (fig. 6.9). Each request asks the child to use the portfolio to accomplish a specific task. Children and teachers can use these requests to assess—

- progress in the development of academic skills or creative talents;
- accomplishment of previously established learning goals;
- the ability to use reflection and self-assessment; and
- the ability to share information with others.

The second stage of the conference occurs within two or three days. At this meeting, we focus on the child's use of the portfolio to fulfill the requests. At the end of the second stage, each child sets new learning goals that can be accomplished before the next portfolio conference. I place one copy of these goals in the portfolio, keep a second copy, and send a third copy home to parents.

Besides their obvious utility for assessment, portfolio conferences are a valuable tool for helping children monitor their own progress, especially in acquiring abilities that develop slowly, such as problem solving. By encouraging reflection and revision, they can also help children see the connections among subject areas. In addition, these one-on-one conversations can foster stronger personal bonds between children and teachers.

## QUESTIONS AND ANSWERS ABOUT ASSESSMENT

### How do you assign letter grades using observations, interviews, rubrics, and portfolios?

Our school has chosen not to use letter grades for reporting progress in mathematics problem solving. Instead, we use a narrative report card, portfolio conferences, and rubrics. This combination of reporting procedures provides more detailed and accurate feedback to both children and parents, makes the teacher's expectations clearer, and supports self-assessment by children.

### If children work together, do they receive the same score?

Yes. If children choose to work together, I remind them that they will receive the same score as their partners.

### Why should children use rubrics?

Children become better problem solvers when they receive feedback that breaks a complex task into its major components. Rubrics provide children with specific and detailed information that can help them improve their performance.

| | 8:30–9:10 | 9:10–9:50 | 9:50–10:30 | 12:30–1:10 | 1:10–1:50 | 1:50–2:30 |
|---|---|---|---|---|---|---|
| **Week 1** | | | | | | |
| Gym | Room 1 | Room 2 | Room 3 | Room 4 | Room 5 | Room 6 |
| Computer Lab | Room 3 | Room 1 | Room 2 | Room 6 | Room 4 | Room 5 |
| Resource Room | Room 2 | Room 3 | Room 1 | Room 5 | Room 6 | Room 4 |
| **Week 2** | | | | | | |
| Gym | Room 7 | Room 8 | Room 9 | Room 10 | Room 11 | Room 12 |
| Computer Lab | Room 8 | Room 9 | Room 7 | Room 11 | Room 12 | Room 10 |
| Resource Room | Room 9 | Room 7 | Room 8 | Room 12 | Room 10 | Room 11 |

Fig. 6.10. Typical schedule for an activities program

## When do you find the time to meet individually with children to conduct portfolio conferences and interviews?

Because our school has recognized the benefits of portfolio conferences and interviews, we have designated time in our schedule for them (see, e.g., fig. 6.10). On Fridays, all the regular physical education, computer lab, and resource room (Title I) classes have been replaced by an activities program. This program is supervised by the Title I staff, consisting of one teacher and five instructional assistants.

A typical Friday scheduling arrangement (as seen in fig. 6.10) gives each teacher two hours every other week for one-on-one assessment while the rest of the class participates in the activities program. Although the list of activities may change from year to year, our program has featured mathematics and language games, computer activities, dance classes, and art lessons, among other offerings. Other schools have adopted similar schedules, but they may include four activities instead of three or may use different instructional staff, such as the principal, counselor, librarian, music teacher, and so on.

## Alternative forms of assessment seem like a lot of work. Don't traditional tests tell teachers what they need to know about children?

I use a balanced evaluation program that integrates traditional tests with alternative performance assessments. Although traditional tests can reveal what children know, performance assessments can more accurately describe what children are able to do with this knowledge.

I have found that performance assessments, such as rubrics and portfolios, invite children to share responsibility for the evaluation process. Traditional tests often treat children as the objects of evaluation; tests are done on or to children. In contrast, performance assessments can be done by children.

When teachers share the responsibility for classroom-level assessment with children, then direct observations, interviews, rubrics, and portfolios can become powerful tools for both teaching and learning.

# 7 USING SHARE AND COMPARE:
## MOVING TO THE EDGE

"Bent Offerings," by Don Addis; reprinted courtesy
of the artist

Imagine a classroom . . . where all students have access to high-quality, engaging mathematics instruction. Students are flexible and resourceful problem solvers. Orally and in writing, students communicate their ideas and results effectively.

—National Council of Teachers of Mathematics,
*Principles and Standards for School Mathematics*

Come to the edge, he said.

They said, we are afraid.

Come to the edge, he said.

They said, we are afraid.

Come to the edge, he said.

They came.

He pushed them . . . and they flew.

—Apollinaire

I have made many mistakes over the years, but like a good problem solver, I have tried to see mistakes as learning opportunities. Some of these mistakes led me to question the wisdom of making problem solving the focus of mathematics activities in my classroom. Was it realistic for me to expect six- and seven-year-old children to engage in a task as demanding as problem solving? The drill-and-practice approach can be repetitious and boring, but it is predictable and precise. By comparison, the complexity of problem solving can be frustrating, especially for young children struggling to make sense of their world.

I doubted myself, but my doubts were laid to rest on the day I read the following poem written by three children in our classroom. It contains good advice for problem solvers of all ages:

When I am patient

I'm careful and slow.

When I am persistent

always forward I go.

I know that with practice

I'll be the best I can be.

And with a positive attitude

I can do it. Trust me.

From that day on, I never looked back—and I know I never will.

## HELPFUL HINTS FOR PULLING IT ALL TOGETHER

*Start small.* Create an environment that is comfortable for you and the children by acting slowly and deliberately. Let the culture of the classroom take on a life of its own. To teach problem solving effectively, you need to learn to trust in your own abilities as well as in those of your students. Several years may be needed to transform a classroom into a community of problem solvers.

*Introduce the four main activities of the share-and-compare model in this order: warm-up, problem for the day, mathematician's chair, and compare.* Start with some daily warm-up activities, including problems that build flexibility and fluency. Gradually add a few mental math exercises and some easy-to-solve problems. Ask children to share their solutions with a partner and explain why they agree or disagree with their partner's solution. Next introduce children to challenging problems through the use of children's literature or questions that arise in the classroom. Encourage children to solve problems in ways that make sense to them and to record their solutions using the show-and-tell approach described in chapter 2. When children are comfortable solving problems on their own, ask them to share and compare their solutions in the mathematician's chair.

*Practice the role of facilitator during mathematician's chair.* Most children know how to talk, but few know how to discuss. The share-and-compare model provides both the framework and the opportunity for classroom conversations. However, good discussions also require good listening skills and good speaking skills. Since most young children lack these skills, teachers must model them. "Students do not necessarily talk about mathematics naturally; teachers need to help them learn how to do so" (NCTM 2000, p. 60).

*Learn to value diversity.* When every student solves a problem using the same standardized procedure, not much arises to talk about. When children share different ways of solving a problem, the diversity of perspectives can increase every student's understanding. Sharing a wide variety of solutions gives children the chance to hear new ideas, learn useful problem-solving strategies, and discover errors in their logic (NCTM 2000).

*Learn to value mistakes.* Mistakes are the stepping stones to new understanding. When a child gives an incorrect answer, you can transform the mistake into a new problem for the whole class to solve by asking,

"What problem did she solve?" or "What question did he answer?" Mistakes add vitality to discussions and are reliable indicators of children's current levels of understanding. When you are trying to extend and expand children's knowledge, mistakes are a good place to start.

*Learn to model the disposition of a problem solver.* Be *patient.* Some children need more time than others to collect their thoughts, solve problems, and share their ideas. Be *perseverant.* Some children adopt a sense of "learned helplessness," especially in mathematics. Teach them to trust in themselves. Be *positive.* Some children fear mathematics and need a positive role model.

*Learn to ask good questions.* Ask children questions, even when they have solved problems correctly. Many children believe that the only time a teacher questions their solution is when they make a mistake. When children learn that your questions help to clarify your understanding of their solution process, their understanding deepens as well. During mathematician's chair, ask children to respond to one another's comments, to summarize ideas, and to compare solutions.

*Learn that less is more.* The insights children gain by solving a single problem using sense making can prove more valuable than many hours of drill and practice. Workbook exercises can help children acquire the conventions of mathematics, but children "who memorize facts or procedures without understanding often are not sure when or how to use what they know, and such learning is often quite fragile" (NCTM 2000, p. 20).

*Value collaboration instead of competition.* Collaboration builds a sense of community, whereas competition can lead to a sense of conflict. Research has shown that competition reduces risk taking, creativity, and a willingness to share—three essential ingredients for successful problem solving (Kohn 1986). Try to value ideas without judging them, and show children how to discuss ideas without criticizing individuals. Demonstrate genuine interest in what children say and do, offer support when needed, and practice the fine art of "stepping back" so that children can discover things on their own.

*Join with colleagues to form a support group.* Just as children become better problem solvers when they share and compare solutions, teachers become better facilitators when they share and compare successful classroom practices. "Most mathematics teachers work in relative isolation, with little support for innovation and few incentives to improve their practice. Yet much of teachers' best learning occurs when they examine their teaching practices with colleagues" (NCTM 2000, p. 370).

*Reflect on your progress.* Use one of the self-assessment checklists shown in Appendix 7 to measure your growth as a teacher of problem solving.

In my classroom, children learn that mathematics is useful for solving a wide range of problems. They learn that mathematics makes sense and that they should expect it to make sense. Because the classroom culture supports their efforts to communicate their thinking clearly and completely, children learn that mathematics is a language—a way of organizing, displaying, and communicating ideas. Because classroom activities make connections between mathematics and other subject areas, children learn that mathematics is the science of patterns, structure, and regularity.

A leading mathematics educator has argued that arithmetic is the cornerstone of mathematics. I agree with this sentiment. But if arithmetic is the cornerstone, then problem solving is the foundation, mortar, and capstone for constructing understanding in mathematics. The share-and-compare model offers a blueprint for building this understanding.

# APPENDIX 1
## A CONVERSATION WITH THE AUTHOR

### HOW LONG HAVE YOU BEEN TEACHING?

I have been teaching for twenty-six years. I started my career as a very traditional mathematics teacher. The children in my classroom completed paper-and-pencil computational exercises, fact drills, and frequent quizzes called "mathematics races." Problem solving was limited to the dreaded story problems that appeared every so often at the end of each chapter in the workbook. I now call this instructional model "tell and compel." Most children seemed to do fine with this approach, but I was troubled by these facts:

- Many children needed continual review in order to retain what they were learning.

- Each time the computational exercises changed ever so slightly, it was like starting over. Although the curriculum was organized around a carefully arranged scope and sequence, many children could not seem to build on their previous knowledge.

- Worst of all, when children were given the simplest story problems, most could not apply the mathematics facts and computational algorithms that they had practiced. Very little of what they were learning seemed to transfer outside the narrow context in which it was learned.

### WHAT GRADE DO YOU CURRENTLY TEACH, AND HOW MANY CHILDREN DO YOU HAVE IN YOUR CLASSROOM?

I currently teach thirty-one children in a multiage classroom, grades 1–3. However, I have spent most of my career in single-grade classrooms (grades 2, 3, or 6). I chose to move to a multiage classroom about seven years ago because I found that young problem solvers benefit from being in the company of more experienced practitioners. These older peers can model the process of solving problems and provide feedback in a way that younger children readily accept and understand.

### WHERE DO YOU TEACH?

I teach at Jefferson Elementary School in Jefferson, Oregon. Once a rural township, Jefferson has become a bedroom community for the nearby cities of Albany and Salem. The town has one main street lined with old, boarded-up stores. A few local families are wealthy farmers. Some of the families are in the working class and struggle to make ends meet, but many families are on welfare. Class sizes range from twenty-eight to thirty children. Jefferson Elementary has been a Title I school for several years.

### WILL THE SHARE-AND-COMPARE MODEL WORK IN A SINGLE-GRADE CLASSROOM?

Yes. In fact, most of the model's development was carried out in a single-grade classroom over a period of four years, two in a second-grade classroom and two in a third-grade classroom.

### YOU MENTIONED THAT SOME ASPECTS OF THE TELL-AND-COMPEL APPROACH FOR TEACHING MATHEMATICS TROUBLED YOU. CAN YOU ELABORATE ON YOUR CONCERNS A LITTLE MORE?

At first, I thought the children were experiencing difficulty because they were young and inexperienced. I thought that if I did my job well, the understanding would come later in school. Then I discovered that middle school and high school teachers shared the same concerns.

One of the reasons that the traditional approach has been used by so many teachers, and for so long, is that it works. Tell-and-compel is a successful, logical, and efficient way to teach arithmetic skills to most children. However, it is *not* an effective approach for helping most children learn the following skills:

- How to communicate their thoughts to others
- How to do mathematics with confidence
- How to become problem solvers

The tell-and-compel approach can also have some unexpected and unintended consequences, especially when used with beginning problem solvers:

- Young children can learn that mathematics is not supposed to make sense; it is supposed to be memorized.
- Young children can become dependent on their teacher to show them what to do rather than learn how to use logic and reason to solve problems.
- Young children can learn to distrust their own natural problem-solving abilities.
- Young children can develop "math phobia." For a complete description of math phobia, you may wish to examine *Math: Facing an American Phobia,* by Marilyn Burns (1998).

Considering these consequences, I gradually began to replace workbook exercises with other activities that were more effective in helping children understand mathematics. First I used mathematics games to make learning more fun. Next I used manipulatives so that children would have "hands-on experiences." Finally I tried making every Friday "problem-solving day." Through these experiments, I learned that the traditional drill-and-practice model of instruction does not work well for teaching problem solving. So I set out to create a model that would work.

## YOU SAID THAT YOU CREATED THIS MODEL BY USING ACTION RESEARCH. WHAT IS ACTION RESEARCH, AND HOW DOES IT DIFFER FROM TRADITIONAL RESEARCH?

Action research is the process of asking a worthwhile research question, collecting credible evidence to answer this question, and using that evidence to guide further improvement in classroom practices. The biggest difference between action research and traditional research lies in the outcomes that each strives to achieve. The goal of action research is primarily directed toward meeting the specific needs of children within the classroom of the teacher-researcher, whereas the goal of traditional research is directed toward meeting the needs of children in general.

Action research gives teachers a chance to investigate what really works in the classroom and to examine why it works. In addition, action research expands what it means to be a teacher. It is more than professional development—it is about improving the essence of teaching. When I share the results of my research, I am forced to clarify my thoughts and to practice the art of reflection. Action research is about transforming teachers into active participants in the construction of their own knowledge. By engaging in action research, I learned that good research questions are the seeds from which real understanding can take root and grow.

As a novice researcher, I made many mistakes. The first mistake involved not knowing where to begin. I thought I should start by trying out something new. As Marcel Proust observed, however, "The real voyage of discovery lies not in seeking new landscapes but in having new eyes" (Ryan in Gozdz 1995, p. 91). Eventually, I learned to look closely at my own practices rather than experiment with new ideas.

Another mistake involved not knowing when to end. I thought that my research was finished when I answered my question. However, I discovered that action research is much like the Japanese practice of *kaizen,* which means "reform through continuous improvement." (In contrast, some schools in the United States seem to engage in the practice of "reform through continuous change.") Over time, I learned to modify my original question rather than ask an entirely new one.

Action research is not the latest educational fad. Nearly seventy years ago, John Dewey reminded teachers that they should investigate interesting research questions and explore new ways of teaching—that they should be scholars, not technicians (Dewey 1933). In short, Dewey challenged teachers to be students of teaching. Traditional research educates teachers from the outside in, by extending what they know. Action research educates teachers from the inside out, by expanding what they understand.

## CAN YOU DESCRIBE YOUR ACTION RESEARCH PROJECT IN MORE DETAIL?

I began the project with the help of Ken Winograd at Oregon State University. Professor Winograd had formed an action-research group consisting of professors, college students, and classroom teachers. The group met monthly for about two years to share the results of individual research projects and to provide support and encouragement for group members. Although this group disbanded, I continued my research. More than 300 children have participated in the project, now in its tenth year.

My focus has differed from that of other researchers in several significant ways. I have examined, and continue to examine,

- beginning problem solvers in the primary grades rather than older students;
- changes in children's performance over a two- or three-year period in a multiage classroom;
- how children learn to become problem solvers by solving problems in ways that make sense to them rather than by being taught heuristics and tradition-al problem-solving strategies;
- the social aspects of the classroom environment that facilitate problem solving rather than examine individual children as they solve problems.

I document changes in children's performance through direct observation, interviews, scoring guides, and portfolios. My students' progress is also evaluated annually using the Oregon + Test (Microsystems for Education & Business) and the Oregon Statewide Assessment Program (State of Oregon Department of Education). I document the changes in my own beliefs and classroom practices using a journal.

# Appendix 2
## Flexibility and Fluency Overheads

What do you see?

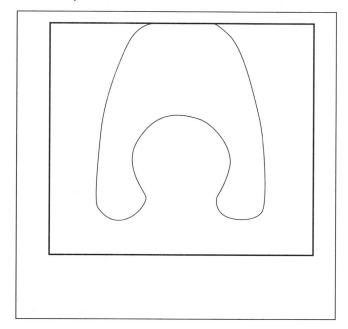

What do you see?

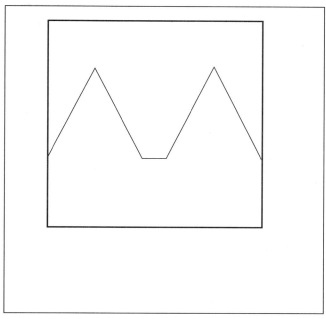

What do you see?

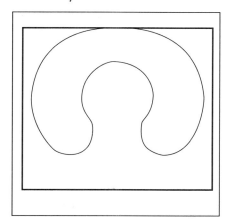

What do you see?

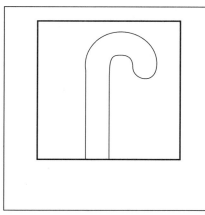

What do you see?

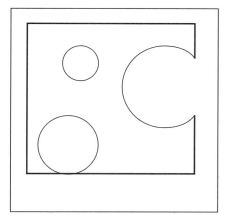

What do you see?

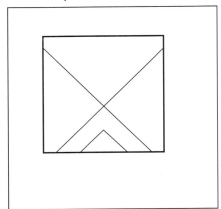

What do you see?

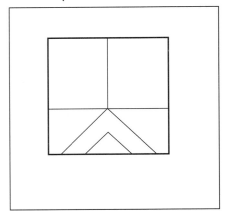

What do you see?

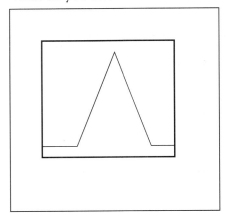

What do you see?

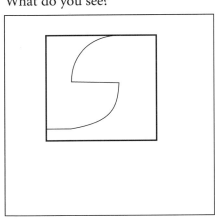

What do you see?

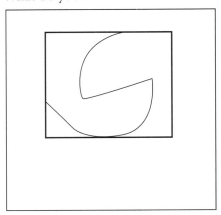

What do you see?

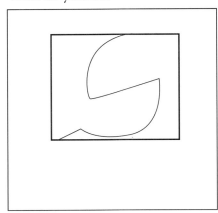

What do you see?

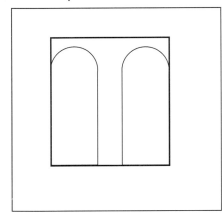

What do you see?

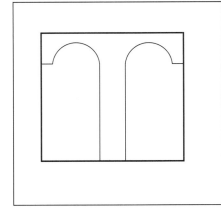

What do you see?

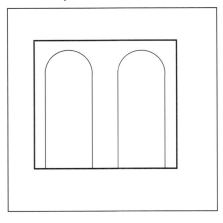

What do you see?

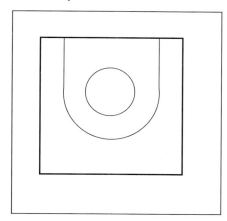

What do you see?

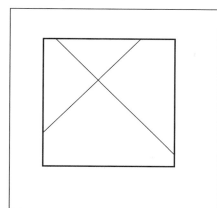

What do you see?

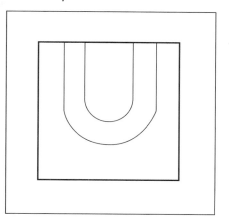

What do you see?

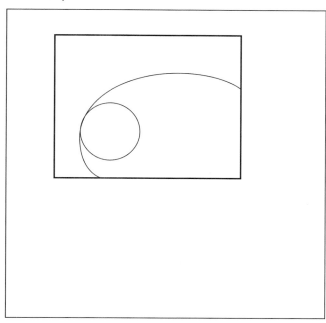

What do you see?

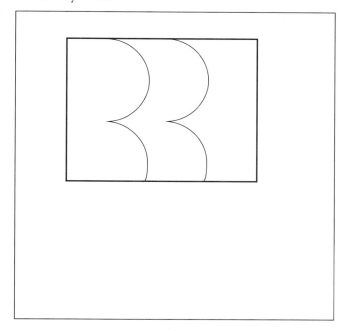

# APPENDIX 3
## IDEAS FOR BOOKS BY CHILDREN

Encouraging children to write their own books is a wonderful way for whole language to meet whole mathematics. In my classroom, children write and illustrate their books in two to five days using paper, pencils, crayons, markers, or computers. Here are brief descriptions of several book ideas.

## OPPOSITES

Children make lists of mathematical terms and their opposites, such as small/large, slow/fast, more/less, add/subtract, full/empty, and so on. To begin the book, children use one of the terms in a sentence. On the following page, they use the term's opposite. When children read their books aloud, they ask listeners to predict the "opposite" words.

## MEASUREMENT

This type of book offers many different opportunities for making and recording measurements. You may wish to suggest the following:

- The height and width of objects in the classroom, school, or home
- The weight, volume, or temperature of objects
- Scale maps of the classroom, playground, or other locations
- The time needed to complete various tasks or activities (fifty jumps, for example)
- The activities that can be completed in a specified amount of time

## ABC

Children create an ABC book that uses mathematical terms; for example, "A is for addition that we do each day," "B is for balance that we use to weigh things," and so on. We sometimes complete this book as a collaborative project, with each child contributing one page.

## SHAPES

Children identify the geometric shapes of familiar objects; for example, "A triangle can be a roof on a house" or "A rhombus can be part of a baseball field."

## COUNTING

Each page of this book features a different number of items to count. The project works especially well at holidays. For example, children can write their own versions of "The Twelve Days of Christmas."

## MY SCHOOL COUNTS

Children complete pages with mathematical information about their school; for example, "This is my classroom. It has 26 desks" or "This is my school bus. It has 6 tires."

## MY WEEK IN REVIEW

Children keep a log of their activities during the week, then list mathematical information about some of these events; for example, "On Monday at 8:10 A.M., I ate two bowls of cereal."

## ONLY ONE

This idea has been borrowed from *Only One*, by Marc Harshman and Barbara Garrison (New York: Scholastic, 1993). On each page, children write such sentences as "There may be 375 children, but there is only one school."

## NUMBERS

Children select a single number as the book's title and theme. For example, a page in a *Four Book* might read "A horse has four legs."

## CURTAINS

In this book, children complete the following sentence on each page:

There are _____ animals and _____ legs behind the curtain.

What animals do you think are behind the curtain?

A drawing of the required number of animals is concealed by a paper curtain, which can be raised to reveal the answer.

## RIDDLES

Children create a book of mathematical riddles; for example, "I am between 0 and 20. I am an even number. What am I?" (Each riddle does not necessarily have a single correct answer.)

## DICTIONARY

Using the dictionary format, children list words from a particular unit or topic. For example, children can make shape dictionaries, pattern dictionaries, and so on.

## AT THE MALL

In our version of this project, each page displays a stick figure to which children add an article of clothing. Children use newspapers or catalogs to determine the cost of each item, then complete the following sentence:

At the _____ I bought _____ for _____.

For example, "At the shoe store, I bought basketball shoes for $39.95." Authors may ask readers to determine the total amount spent at the mall.

# Lift Tabs

Children create a collection of story problems, with the answers hidden under paper tabs (see fig. A3.1). When reading aloud, the author encourages listeners to predict each answer before lifting the tab.

Fig. A3.1. Page from a lift-tab book

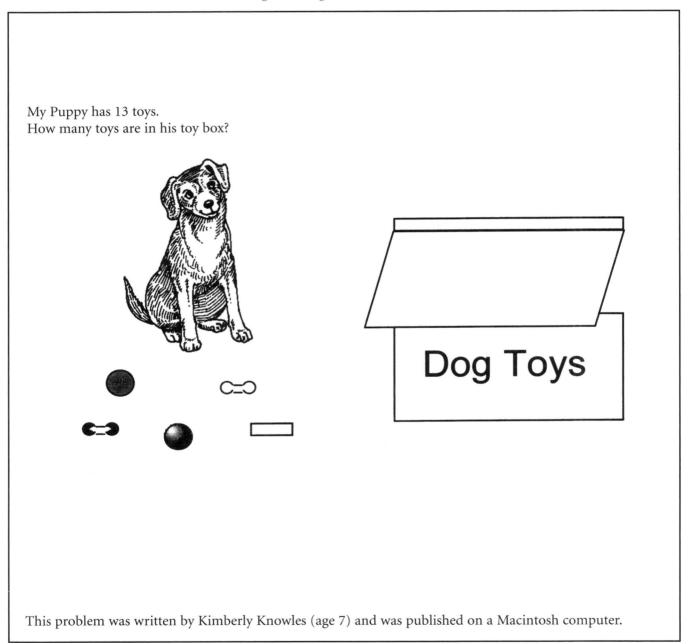

My Puppy has 13 toys.
How many toys are in his toy box?

Dog Toys

This problem was written by Kimberly Knowles (age 7) and was published on a Macintosh computer.

# PULL TABS

Although a favorite with children, these books can be difficult to make. Like lift-tab books, they contain a collection of story problems. Each answer is revealed by pulling a picture from a slot in the page (see fig. A3.2).

Fig. A3.2. Pages from a pull-tab book

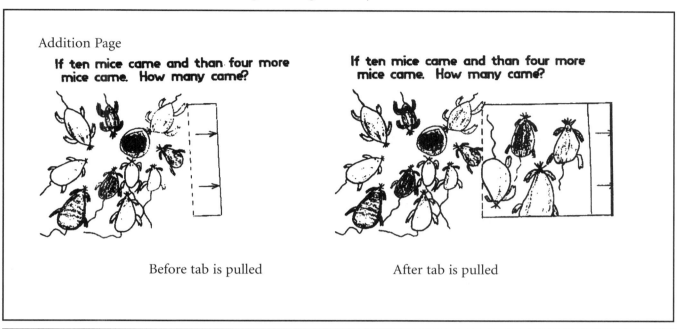

Addition Page

If ten mice came and than four more mice came. How many came?

Before tab is pulled

If ten mice came and than four more mice came. How many came?

After tab is pulled

Subtraction Page

If 12 elephants came for a drink and 6 went away. How many are left?

Before tab is pulled

If 12 elephants came for a drink and 6 went away. How many are left?

After tab is pulled

These pages were authored by Andy Loika and Kyle Bingham (both age 7).

# APPENDIX 4

## CHILDREN'S LITERATURE

Aker, Suzanne. *What Comes in 2's, 3's, and 4's?* Illustrated by Bernie Karlin. New York: Scholastic, 1990.

Allen, Pamela. *Mr. Archimedes' Bath.* Melbourne, Australia: Angus & Robertson, 1980.

Anno, Mitsumasa. *Anno's Counting Book.* New York: Scholastic, 1995.

Ash, Russell. *Incredible Comparisons.* New York: DK Publishing, 1996.

Ata, Te., and Lynn Moroney. *Baby Rattlesnake.* Illustrated by Mira Reisberg. San Francisco, Calif.: Children's Book Press, 1989.

Axelrod, Amy. *Pigs Will Be Pigs.* Illustrated by Sharon McGinley-Nally. New York: The Trumpet Club, 1994.

Baker, Keith. *Hide and Snake.* New York: The Trumpet Club, 1991.

Banyai, Istvan. *Zoom.* New York: Viking, 1995.

Barner, Bob. *Space Race.* New York: Bantam Doubleday Dell, 1995.

———. *Too Many Dinosaurs.* New York: Bantam Doubleday Dell, 1995.

———. *Dinosaurs Depart.* New York: Bantam Doubleday Dell, 1996.

Barrett, Judi. *Things That Are Most in the World.* New York: Atheneum Books for Young Readers, 1998.

Baylor, Byrd. *Everybody Needs a Rock.* Illustrated by Peter Parnail. New York: Aladdin Paperbacks, 1974.

Birch, David, and Devis Grebu. *The King's Chessboard.* New York: Puffin Pied Piper Books, 1988.

Birmingham, Duncan. *"M" Is for Mirror.* Stradbroke, U.K.: Tarquin, 1988.

———. *Look Twice.* Stradbroke, U.K.: Tarquin, 1992.

Blumenthal, Nancy. *Count-A-Saurus.* Illustrated by Robert J. Kaufman. New York: Scholastic, 1989.

Bridwell, Norman. *Clifford at the Circus.* New York: Scholastic, 1985.

Briggs, Raymond. *Jim and the Beanstalk.* New York: Putnam, 1989.

Brisson, Pat. *Benny's Pennies.* New York: Dell Books for Young Readers, 1993.

Brown, Margaret Wise. *Goodnight Moon.* Illustrated by Clement Hurd. New York: Harper & Row, 1974.

———. *The Greedy Triangle.* Illustrated by Gordon Silveria. New York: Scholastic, 1994.

Burns, Marilyn. *Spaghetti and Meatballs for All!* New York: Scholastic, 1997.

Butterworth, Nick. *Jasper's Beanstalk.* New York: Aladdin Paperbacks, 1993.

Carle, Eric. *1, 2, 3 to the Zoo.* New York: The Trumpet Club, 1968.

———. *The Grouchy Ladybug.* New York: Harper Trophy, 1977.

Carlson, Nancy. *Harriet's Halloween Candy.* Minneapolis, Minn.: Carolrhoda Books, 1982.

Christelow, Eileen. *Five Little Monkeys Sitting in a Tree.* New York: The Trumpet Club, 1991.

Chwast, Seymour. *The 12 Circus Rings.* New York: Gulliver Books, 1993.

Clement, Rod. *Counting on Frank.* Milwaukee, Wis.: Gareth Stevens, 1991.

Cleveland, David. *The April Rabbits.* Illustrated by Nurit Kurlin. New York: Scholastic, 1978.

Cooney, Barbara. *Miss Rumphius.* New York: Puffin Books, 1985.

Crews, Donald. *Ten Black Dots.* New York: Scholastic, 1968.

———. *Freight Train.* New York: Mulberry Books, 1978.

Ehlert, Lois. *Color Zoo.* New York: The Trumpet Club, 1989.

———. *Color Farm.* New York: Harper Collins, 1990.

Ernst, Lisa Campbell. *Up to Ten and Down Again.* New York: Mulberry Books, 1986.

Friedman, Aileen. *A Cloak for the Dreamer.* Illustrated by Kim Howard. New York: Scholastic, 1994.

———. *The King's Commissioners.* Illustrated by Susan Guevara. New York: Scholastic, 1994.

Giganti, Paul Jr. *How Many Snails?* Edited by Amy Cohn and illustrated by Donald Crews. New York: The Trumpet Club, 1988.

———. *Each Orange Had 8 Slices.* New York: The Trumpet Club, 1992.

———. *Notorious Numbers*. San Leandro, Calif.: Teaching Resource Center, 1993.

Ginsburg, Mirra. *The Old Man and His Birds*. New York: Greenwillow Books, 1994.

Gomi, Taro. *Spring Is Here*. New York: The Trumpet Club, 1989.

Grossman, Virginia. *Ten Little Rabbits*. Illustrated by Sylvia Long. New York: The Trumpet Club, 1991.

Grover, Max. *Amazing and Incredible Counting Stories*. Lake Oswego, Ore.: Browndeer Press, 1995.

Harshman, Marc, and Barbara Garrison. *Only One*. New York: Scholastic, 1993.

Hindley, Judy. *The Wheeling and Whirling-Around Book*. Cambridge, Mass.: Candlewick Books, 1994.

Hoban, Tana. *26 Letters and 99 Cents*. New York: Scholastic, 1987.

Hodgson, Jim. *Numberland: Lift-the-Flap*. Dorking, U.K.: The Templar Co., 1995.

Hulme, Joy N. *Sea Squares*. Illustrated by Carol Schwartz. New York: Hyperion Paperbacks for Children, 1991.

———. *Counting by Kangaroos*. New York: W. H. Freeman & Co., 1995.

———. *Sea Sums*. New York: Hyperion Books for Children, 1996.

Hutchins, Pat. *The Doorbell Rang*. New York: Mulberry Books, 1986.

———. *Clocks and More Clocks*. New York: Aladdin Books, 1994.

Jenkins, Steve. *Biggest, Strongest, Fastest*. New York: Ticknor & Fields Books for Young Readers, 1995.

———. *Big and Little*. Boston, Mass.: Houghton Mifflin Co., 1996.

———. *Hottest, Coldest, Highest, Deepest*. Boston, Mass.: Houghton Mifflin Co., 1998.

Jonas, Ann. *Round Trip*. New York: Mulberry Books, 1983.

———. *Splash*. New York: Greenwillow Books, 1995.

Joyce, William. *George Shrinks*. New York: Scholastic, 1985.

Kalan, Robert. *Jump, Frog, Jump*. Illustrated by Byron Barton. New York: Scholastic, 1981.

Kellogg, Steven. *Much Bigger Than Martin*. New York: The Trumpet Club, 1976.

Leedy, Loreen. *Fraction Action*. New York: Holiday House, 1994.

———. *Measuring Penny*. New York: Henry Holt & Co., 1997.

Legge, David. *Bamboozled*. New York: Scholastic, 1994.

Lindbergh, Reeve. *The Midnight Farm*. New York: Dial Books for Young Readers, 1987.

Lionni, Leo. *Inch by Inch*. New York: Mulberry Books, 1960.

Lottridge, Celia Barker. *One Watermelon Seed*. Illustrated by Karen Patkau. Toronto: Oxford University Press, 1986.

MacDonald, Suse. *Alphabatics*. New York: The Trumpet Club, 1986.

———. *Sea Shapes*. New York: Gulliver Books, 1994.

Mahy, Margaret. *17 Kings and 42 Elephants*. New York: Dial Books for Young Readers, 1987.

Manushkin, Fran. *Walt Disney's 101 Dalmatians: A Counting Book*. Illustrated by Russell Hicks. New York: The Trumpet Club, 1991.

Maris, Ron. *Better Move On Frog*. San Diego, Calif.: Harcourt Brace Jovanovich, 1989.

Marshall, Janet. *Look Once, Look Twice*. New York: Ticknor & Fields Books for Young Readers, 1995.

Martin, Bill Jr., and John Archambault. *Knots on a Counting Rope*. Illustrated by Ted Rand. New York: The Trumpet Club, 1987.

Marzollo, Jean. *Sun Song*. Illustrated by Laura Regan. New York: Harper Collins, 1995.

McDermott, Gerald. *Arrow to the Sun*. New York: Puffin Books, 1974.

McGrath, Barbara Barbieri. *The M&M's Brand Counting Book*. Watertown, Mass.: Charlesbridge, 1994.

McKissack, Patricia C. *A Million Fish . . . More or Less*. New York: Alfred A. Knopf, 1992.

Merriam, Eve. *12 Ways to Get to 11*. Illustrated by Bernie Karlin. New York: The Trumpet Club, 1993.

Min, Laura. *Mrs. Sato's Hens*. Illustrated by Benrei Huang. Redding, Calif.: Good Year Books, 1994.

Moore, Inga. *Six Dinner Sid*. New York: Simon & Schuster Books for Young Readers, 1991.

Morgan, Rowland. *In the Next Three Seconds*. New York: Lodestar Books, 1997.

Murphy, Chuck. *My First Book of Shapes*. New York: Scholastic, 1992.

Murphy, Stuart J. *Betcha!* New York: Harper Collins, 1997.

———. *Divide and Ride*. New York: Harper Collins, 1997.

Myller, Rolf. *How Big Is a Foot?* New York: Dell Publishing, 1990.

Neuschwander, Cindy. *Amanda Bean's Amazing Dream*. New York: Scholastic Press, 1998.

Owen, Annie. *Annie's ABC*. New York: The Trumpet Club, 1987.

Pallotta, Jerry. *The Icky Bug Counting Book*. Illustrated by Ralph Masiello. New York: The Trumpet Club, 1992.

Paul, Ann Whitford. *Eight Hands Round*. New York: Harper Collins, 1991.

Pinczes, Elinor J. *One Hundred Hungry Ants*. Boston, Mass.: Houghton Mifflin Co., 1983.

———. *A Remainder of One*. New York: Scholastic, 1995.

Reid, Margarette S. *The Button Box*. New York: Puffin Unicorn Books, 1990.

Ryan, Pam Munoz. *The Crayon Counting Book.* Watertown, Mass.: Charlesbridge, 1996.

Schlein, Miriam. *More Than One.* New York: Greenwillow Books, 1996.

Schwartz, David M. *How Much Is a Million?* Illustrated by Steven Kellog. New York: Scholastic, 1985.

———. *If You Made a Million.* New York: Scholastic, 1989.

Scieszka, Jon. *Math Curse.* Illustrated by Lane Smith. New York: Viking, 1995.

Seuss, Dr. *The Foot Book.* New York: Random House, 1968.

Sharratt, Nick. *My Mom and Dad Make Me Laugh.* Cambridge, Mass.: Candlewick Press, 1994.

Sloat, Teri. *From One to One Hundred.* New York: Scholastic, 1991.

Steig, William. *Sylvester and the Magic Pebble.* New York: Simon & Schuster, 1969.

Tompert, Ann. *Grandfather Tang's Story.* New York: Crown Publishers, 1990.

Torres, Leyla. *Saturday Sancocho.* New York: Farrar Straus Giroux, 1995.

Van Fleet, Matthew. *One Yellow Lion.* New York: Dial Books for Young Readers, 1992.

———. *Fuzzy Yellow Ducklings.* New York: Dial Books for Young Readers, 1995.

———. *Spotted Yellow Frogs.* New York: Dial Books for Young Readers, 1998.

Viorst, Judith. *Alexander, Who Used to Be Rich Last Sunday.* Illustrated by R. Cruz. New York: Scholastic, 1978.

Waite, Judy. *Mouse, Look Out!* New York: Dutton Children's Books, 1998.

Wells, Robert E. *Is a Blue Whale the Biggest Thing There Is?* New York: Scholastic, 1993.

Wells, Rosemary. *Bunny Money.* New York: Dial Books for Young Readers, 1997.

Wise, William. *Ten Sly Piranhas.* Illustrated by Victoria Chess. New York: Scholastic, 1993.

Wood, Audrey. *Rude Giants.* New York: The Trumpet Club, 1993.

## RESOURCES FOR USING CHILDREN'S LITERATURE

Braddon, Kathryn L. *Math through Children's Literature.* Lebanon, Ind.: Dale Seymour Publications, 1989.

Bresser, Rusty. *Math and Literature (4–6).* Sausalito, Calif.: Math Solutions, 1992.

Burns, Marilyn. *Math and Literature (K–3).* Book One. Sausalito, Calif.: Math Solutions, 1992.

Sheffield, Stephanie. *Math and Literature (K–3).* Book Two. Sausalito, Calif.: Math Solutions, 1992.

Whitin, David, and Sandra Wilde. *Read Any Good Math Lately?: Children's Books for Mathematical Learning, K–6.* Portsmouth, N.H.: Heinemann, 1991.

# APPENDIX 5
## SOURCES OF PROBLEMS

# APPENDIX 5.1
## COMMUNICATION STRUCTURES

## Structure 1

Present a problem along with a solution by an imaginary person. Ask students to write letters to this person, explaining why they agree or disagree with the solution.

## Structure 2

Present a problem and solution in which the solution contains a significant error. Ask students a series of questions designed to reveal their ability to understand and correct the error.

## Structure 3

Present a group of problems with solutions in which some errors occur. Ask students to write letters to this problem solver, describing the errors and explaining how to correctly solve similar problems.

## Structure 4

Present a problem with all of its facts and conditions. Ask each student to write a new problem for this situation, solve it, then explain why the new problem was more difficult or less difficult than the original.

## Structure 5

Present a problem with all of its facts and conditions. Ask students to write several appropriate questions for this situation.

## Structure 6

Present a problem along with a partial solution. Ask students to complete the solution.

## Structure 7

Present a problem that includes facts unrelated to the question. Ask students to identify these facts and to rewrite the problem using only the relevant information.

## Structure 8

Present a problem. Ask students to explain how to solve the problem using words alone. Then ask students to write and solve similar problems.

## Structure 9

After students have solved a problem, ask them to write similar problems that involve different contexts.

## Structure 10

Present a problem for which the numbers have been omitted. Ask students to determine appropriate numbers, then solve the problem.

## Structure 11

Present a graph. Ask students to write stories that correspond with the information on the graph.

## Structure 12

Present a table. Ask students to write stories that correspond with the information in the table.

## Structure 13

Present some sample data. Ask students to discuss the appropriate use of this information for making predictions.

## Structure 14

Present an equation or set of number facts. Ask students to write a story problem that corresponds with this information.

## Structure 15

Present a problem that involves a business or consumer context, including buying, selling, or measuring.

## Structure 16

Ask students to design and conduct a survey on an interesting topic, then report their findings to another classroom.

## Structure 17

Ask students to write problems in the form of a riddle.

## Structure 18

Present a problem that requires students to share items in the classroom or on the playground. Ask students to devise and test their plans for sharing.

## Structure 19

Ask each student to write and publish an original story problem in letter form.

## Structure 20

Present an open-ended problem. Ask students to consider the problem, then make a written or oral request for the information they think is necessary to solve the problem.

## Structure 21

Ask students to rewrite a familiar folk tale, adding numerical information. Then ask students to use their versions to create story problems.

# APPENDIX 5.2
## PROBLEMS WRITTEN BY CHILDREN

### PROBLEMS INSPIRED BY A HOLIDAY

*Jori:* If Santa put 2 TVs at the houses. How many TVs are in 10 houses?

*Caitlin:* Mrs. Claus made sandwiches for her wonderful elves. She made 24 sandwiches out of 2 loaves of bread. How many pieces of bread are in a loaf that she used to make sandwiches?

*Katrina:* Santa has 30 reindeers and half of them calved. How many reindeers does he have now?

*Patrick:* Santa weighs twice as much as one reindeer. Five reindeer weigh in at 450 pounds. How much does Santa weigh?

### PROBLEMS INSPIRED BY A SHORT STORY

Every day, Freddy Frog gets up and goes jumping to stay in shape. He jumps 5 times, and then he rests for 1 minute. Then he jumps 10 times and rests for 2 minutes. Finally, he jumps 15 times and goes home to take a shower. One day his wife asked him, "How far do you jump each day, my dear?" Freddy Frog didn't know, because he only counted the number of jumps. He had never measured how far he jumped. The next day he took a measuring tape with him. When he was ready, he made his first jump. He jumped 3 feet. Every time he jumped, he went the same distance. Now he knows how far he jumps each day.

*Gemma:* How far did he jump before he rested the one minute?

*Justin:* How far did he jump that day?

*Marisa:* One day he hurt his foot and he was crying so he didn't want to go jump but his wife said, "You should get out of the house and do something, so get going you lazy old frog." He couldn't jump so far because he hurt his foot. He jumped 5 inches. How far did he jump the day he hurt his foot?

*Brett:* How far does he jump in a week?

### PROBLEMS INSPIRED BY AN ANSWER (2-1/2 DOZEN COOKIES)

*Cris:* I have 10 dozen cookies. I gave half of them to the kids at school. Then I gave half of them to the kids at church. How much do I have left?

*Shanna:* My mom baked 3 dozen cookies for the store. If there are 6 cookies in each bag and if one person bought 1 bag for $3.00, how many cookies were left?

*Micah:* I have 100 cookies. I eat 90 cookies. I make 20 more cookies. I eat 6-1/2 cookies and sell 3-1/2 cookies. I buy 10 cookies. How many dozen cookies do I have?

*Stefani:* The snack packs have 4 cookies. I bought 7-1/2 snack packs. How many dozens of cookies is that?

# APPENDIX 5.3
## COMICS

Comics can be found in newspapers, in books, or on the Internet. (As of this printing, I recommend www.pen.k12.va.us/Div/Winchester/jhhs/math/humor/comics/arith/perc10.html.)

- Calvin thinks he will have more than $150 after 1 year. Write Calvin a letter and tell him why you agree or disagree with his answer.
- If Calvin put 1 tooth under his pillow every night for 1 year, and the tooth fairy leaves 50 cents for each tooth, how much will Calvin earn in 1 year?
- Since Hobbes is a tiger, he has 34 teeth. How much could Hobbes earn if he put all his teeth under his pillow and the tooth fairy leaves 75 cents for each tooth?
- Calvin put one fake tooth under his pillow each night. After 7 nights, he earned $3.50. How much did the tooth fairy leave for each tooth?
- If each of Calvin's fake teeth weighs 1.5 ounces, how much would 10 fake teeth weigh?

"Okee-doke! Let's just double-check. We're 130 feet up and we've got 45 yards of bungee cord, that's uh ... 90 feet. Allow for 30 feet of stretching, that gives us a total of ... 120 feet. Perfect!"

- Write the characters in the cartoon a letter and tell them why you agree or disagree with their solution to the problem.
- If the rope is 45 yards long and it stretches 30 feet, how tall should the tower be so the jumper never comes closer than 15 feet from the ground?

  What if the rope stretches 50 feet instead of 30 feet; how much taller should the tower be?

  What if the rope stretches 40 feet instead of 30 feet; how much shorter should the tower be?
- A jumper jumped off a tower using a rope 45 yards long. The rope stretched 25 feet. If he landed 15 feet above the ground, how tall is the tower?
- A jumper jumped off a tower 175 feet tall using a rope 40 yards long. If he landed 25 feet above the ground, how much did the rope stretch?
- A jumper jumped off a tower 200 feet tall and landed 25 feet above the ground. If the rope stretched 45 feet, how long was the rope?
- If a boy who weighs 25 pounds makes the rope stretch 5 feet. And a boy who weighs 50 pounds makes the rope stretch 10 feet. And a boy who weighs 100 pounds makes the rope stretch 20 feet. How much would the rope stretch if a man who weighs 200 pounds jumped off the tower?

# APPENDIX 5.4
## THE INTERNET

The Internet is a virtual gold mine of problems. I recommend the following sites:

- *National Council of Teachers of Mathematics* (www.nctm.org)
- *Oregon Council of Teachers of Mathematics* (www.octm.org)
- *AIMS Education Center* (www.aimsedu.org)
- *Figure This* (www.figurethis.org)
- *Aunty Math's Challenges for Kids* (www.dupagechildrensmuseum.org/aunty/get-started.html)
- *Math Forum* (mathforum.org/teachers/elem/projects.html; mathforum.org/teachers/elem/3-5/projects.html; mathforum.org/K12/K12puzzles; mathforum.com/varnelle/index.html; mathforum.com/pow)
- *Ask Dr. Math* (mathforum.org/dr.math)
- *Math Magic!* (mathforum.org/mathmagic/index.html)
- *Mega Math* (www.cs.uidaho.edu/~casey931/mega-math/menu.html)
- *Word Problems for Kids* (www.stfx.ca/special/mathproblems/welcome.html)
- *Mathematics Problem Solving Task Centres* (www.mav.vic.edu.au/PSTC)
- *Breaking Away* (www.math.nmsu.edu/breakingaway/main.html)
- *Math Lessons* (www.rice.edu/%7Elanius/Lessons)
- *Problem of the Week* (www.wits.ac.za/ssproule/pow.htm)
- *Student Authored Problems* (www.nationalmathtrail.com)
- *Kids Math Word Problems* (www.syvum.com/math/wordproblems.html)
- *Brain Teasers* (www.eduplace.com/math/brain/index.html)
- *Math Stories* (www.mathstories.com)
- *Math Mastery* (mathmastery.com)
- *Education Place* (www.eduplace.com/main.html)

The following sites feature hot links to most of the sites listed above, as well as other problems for children to solve:

- *ERIC* (www.ericse.org) [Select Mathematics Education Resources, then Weblinks.]
- *Jackie Cooke's Web Page* (westgresham.gresham.k12.or.us/jcooke/prob.html) [Select Problem Solving Sites.]
- *Math Links* (www.abc.se/~m9847/matre/problem.html)
- *Eisenhower National Clearinghouse* (www.enc.org) [Select Web Links—Math Topics.]

# APPENDIX 5.5
## BOOKS ON PROBLEM SOLVING

Many books include "problem solving" in their titles. The following list includes some I have used in my own classroom:

- *Principles and Standards for School Mathematics* Navigation Series, K–12, by the National Council of Teachers of Mathematics (Reston, Va.: NCTM, 2000).

- *Curriculum and Evaluation Standards for School Mathematics* Addenda Series, K–12, by the National Council of Teachers of Mathematics (Reston, Va.: NCTM, 1991).

- *Problem Box: Elementary Problems, Intermediate Problems, and Secondary Problems,* by the Oregon Council of Teachers of Mathematics (Hood River, Ore.: OCTM, 1992–2001).

- *50 Problem-Solving Lessons,* by Marilyn Burns (Sausalito, Calif.: Math Solutions, 1996).

- Hot Math Topics series, by Carole Greenes, Linda Schulman Dacey, and Rika Spungin (Lebanon, Ind.: Dale Seymour Publications, 1999).

- Math by All Means series, by Marilyn Burns and others (Sausalito, Calif.: Math Solutions, 1993–1997).

- *101 Short Problems,* edited by Jean Kerr Stenmark (Berkeley, Calif.: EQUALS, 1995).

- *Posing Open-ended Questions in the Primary Class-room,* by Christina Myren (San Leandro, Calif.: Teaching Resource Center, 1995).

- Read It! Draw It! Solve It! series, by Elizabeth D. Miller (Lebanon, Ind.: Dale Seymour Publications, 1998).

# APPENDIX 6
## SCORED SOLUTIONS FOR TWO PROBLEMS

The scoring guide (rubric) used here has been modified from a scoring guide published by the Oregon Department of Education (see fig. 6.4).

## MATHEMATICS PROBLEM-SOLVING SCORING GUIDE

| Conceptual Understanding | Process and Strategies | Communication | Dispositions |
|---|---|---|---|
| Interpreting the concepts of the task and translating them into mathematics | Choosing strategies that can work, then carrying them out | Using pictures, symbols, and words to convey the path to the solution | Attitudes and beliefs of a successful problem solver |
| **What?** | **How?** | **Connecting Path** | **Guiding Light** |
| (A) Translation of the task is enhanced through connections with, or extensions to, other mathematical ideas. | (A) Elegant, complex, or enhanced mathematical processes or strategies are completed. | (A) The connecting path is enhanced by graphics or examples, allowing the reader to easily make connections from one thought to another. | (A) Seeks out feedback, takes risks, and builds collaborative relationships. |
| (B) Translation of the task into mathematical concepts is thoroughly developed. | (B) Pictures, models, diagrams, or symbols are thoroughly developed. | (B) The path that connects concepts, strategies, or verification of the solution is thoroughly developed. | (B) Offers useful feedback, accepts suggestions, and displays confidence. |
| (C) Translation of the task into mathematical concepts is complete. | (C) Pictures, models, diagrams, or symbols are complete. | (C) The path that connects concepts, strategies, or verification of the solution is complete. | (C) Actively engages in classroom discourse, listens attentively, shares ideas, and reflects on the ideas of others. |
| (D) Translation of the task into mathematical concepts is partially complete. | (D) Pictures, models, diagrams, or symbols are only partially complete or partially useful. | (D) The path that connects concepts, strategies, or verification of the solution is only partially displayed. | (D) Builds cooperative relationships, asks clarifying questions, and recognizes the positive aspects of mistakes. |
| (E) Translation of the task into mathematical concepts is underdeveloped or flawed. | (E) Pictures, models, diagrams, or symbols are underdeveloped or flawed. | (E) The path that connects concepts, strategies, or verification of the solution is underdeveloped or sketchy. | (E) Recognizes that learning requires personal effort, patience, perseverance, and a positive attitude. |
| (F) Translation of the task uses inappropriate concepts or shows minimal understanding. | (F) Pictures, models, diagrams, or symbols are ineffective, not evident, or in conflict with solution. | (F) The path that connects concepts, strategies, or verification of the solution is ineffective or not evident. | (F) Flexibility, perseverance, and a positive attitude are absent in the solution process. |

## ACCURACY

| (5) The answer is mathematically justifiable and supported by the work. | (4) The answer is adequate or contains only a minor error. | (3) | (2) | (1) The answer is incorrect, incomplete, or conflicts with the work. |
|---|---|---|---|---|

# MARISA

## Legs Problem

$\mathcal{7} \mathcal{C} \mathcal{K} \mathcal{h} \mathcal{z}$

7 chickens

## Cards Problem

*1-19-1994*
I got 59 cards. And 25 kids
I put total ser ckds for
heds

54 packages

Marisa 1-19-1994
I got 59 cards and 25 kids.
I put a lot of circles for
heads.

59 packages

---

# MATHEMATICS PROBLEM-SOLVING SCORING GUIDE

| Conceptual Understanding | Process and Strategies | Communication | Dispositions |
|---|---|---|---|
| Interpreting the concepts of the task and translating them into mathematics | Choosing strategies that can work, then carrying them out | Using pictures, symbols, and words to convey the path to the solution | Attitudes and beliefs of a successful problem solver |
| **What?** | **How?** | **Connecting Path** | **Guiding Light** |
| (A) Translation of the task is enhanced through connections with, or extensions to, other mathematical ideas. | (A) Elegant, complex, or enhanced mathematical processes or strategies are completed. | (A) The connecting path is enhanced by graphics or examples, allowing the reader to easily make connections from one thought to another. | (A) Seeks out feedback, takes risks, and builds collaborative relationships. |
| (B) Translation of the task into mathematical concepts is thoroughly developed. | (B) Pictures, models, diagrams, or symbols are thoroughly developed. | (B) The path that connects concepts, strategies, or verification of the solution is thoroughly developed. | (B) Offers useful feedback, accepts suggestions, and displays confidence. |
| (C) Translation of the task into mathematical concepts is complete. | (C) Pictures, models, diagrams, or symbols are complete. | (C) The path that connects concepts, strategies, or verification of the solution is complete. | (C) Actively engages in classroom discourse, listens attentively, shares ideas, and reflects on the ideas of others. |
| (D) Translation of the task into mathematical concepts is partially complete. | (D) Pictures, models, diagrams, or symbols are only partially complete or partially useful. | (D) The path that connects concepts, strategies, or verification of the solution is only partially displayed. | (D) Builds cooperative relationships, asks clarifying questions, and recognizes the positive aspects of mistakes. |
| (E) Translation of the task into mathematical concepts is underdeveloped or flawed. | (E) Pictures, models, diagrams, or symbols are underdeveloped or flawed. | (E) The path that connects concepts, strategies, or verification of the solution is underdeveloped or sketchy. | (E) Recognizes that learning requires personal effort, patience, perseverance, and a positive attitude. |
| (F) Translation of the task uses inappropriate concepts or shows minimal understanding. | (F) Pictures, models, diagrams, or symbols are ineffective, not evident, or in conflict with solution. | (F) The path that connects concepts, strategies, or verification of the solution is ineffective or not evident. | (F) Flexibility, perseverance, and a positive attitude are absent in the solution process. |

## ACCURACY

| (5) The answer is mathematically justifiable and supported by the work. | (4) The answer is adequate or contains only a minor error. | (1) The answer is incorrect, incomplete, or conflicts with the work. |
|---|---|---|

| Legs Problem | Cards Problem |
|---|---|

Although Marisa's written solutions for both problems received the minimum score in all areas of the scoring guide, they do not show a complete picture of her work. As you may recall from the discussions of Marisa's solutions in chapters 2 and 5, she used manipulatives to directly model her solution process. In both cases, however, she did not fully record the steps in the process on paper.

This discrepancy highlights the need to use a variety of tools, including direct observation, to assess children's problem-solving skills and abilities.

# TIM

## Legs Problem

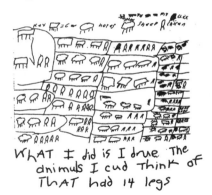

*What I did is I drue The animuls I cud Think of ThAT hAd 14 legs*

What I did is I drew the
animals I could think of that
had 14 legs.

## Cards Problem

*I used A cAcyuLATeV I pushed 25+25=50 And drawed A PiKHuR ThAtshow I Got The Answer 50 lackages*

I used a calculator. After I pushed
25 + 25 = 50 and drawed a
picture that show(s) I got
the answer 50 packages.

---

# MATHEMATICS PROBLEM-SOLVING SCORING GUIDE

| Conceptual Understanding | Process and Strategies | Communication | Dispositions |
|---|---|---|---|
| Interpreting the concepts of the task and translating them into mathematics | Choosing strategies that can work, then carrying them out | Using pictures, symbols, and words to convey the path to the solution | Attitudes and beliefs of a successful problem solver |
| **What?** | **How?** | **Connecting Path** | **Guiding Light** |
| (A) Translation of the task is enhanced through connections with, or extensions to, other mathematical ideas. | (A) Elegant, complex, or enhanced mathematical processes or strategies are completed. | (A) The connecting path is enhanced by graphics or examples, allowing the reader to easily make connections from one thought to another. | (A) Seeks out feedback, takes risks, and builds collaborative relationships. |
| (B) Translation of the task into mathematical concepts is thoroughly developed. | (B) Pictures, models, diagrams, or symbols are thoroughly developed. | (B) The path that connects concepts, strategies, or verification of the solution is thoroughly developed. | (B) Offers useful feedback, accepts suggestions, and displays confidence. |
| (C) ■ Translation of the task into mathematical concepts is complete. | (C) ■ Pictures, models, diagrams, or symbols are complete. | (C) The path that connects concepts, strategies, or verification of the solution is complete. | (C) Actively engages in classroom discourse, listens attentively, shares ideas, and reflects on the ideas of others. |
| (D) Translation of the task into mathematical concepts is partially complete. | (D) Pictures, models, diagrams, or symbols are only partially complete or partially useful. | (D) ■ The path that connects concepts, strategies, or verification of the solution is only partially displayed. | (D) Builds cooperative relationships, asks clarifying questions, and recognizes the positive aspects of mistakes. |
| (E) Translation of the task into mathematical concepts is underdeveloped or flawed. | (E) Pictures, models, diagrams, or symbols are underdeveloped or flawed. | (E) The path that connects concepts, strategies, or verification of the solution is underdeveloped or sketchy. | (E) ■ Recognizes that learning requires personal effort, patience, perseverance, and a positive attitude. |
| (F) Translation of the task uses inappropriate concepts or shows minimal understanding. | (F) Pictures, models, diagrams, or symbols are ineffective, not evident, or in conflict with solution. | (F) The path that connects concepts, strategies, or verification of the solution is ineffective or not evident. | (F) Flexibility, perseverance, and a positive attitude are absent in the solution process. |

## ACCURACY

| (5) The answer is mathematically justifiable and supported by the work. | (4) ■ The answer is adequate or contains only a minor error. | (1) The answer is incorrect, incomplete, or conflicts with the work. |
|---|---|---|

Legs Problem    Cards Problem

Tim's solutions illustrate several important points. For example, his solution to the Legs Problem, which was completed at the beginning of the school year, received higher scores than his solution to the Cards Problem, which was completed several months later. Given this evidence, Tim would appear to be losing ground. However, a more likely explanation for the decrease in scores lies in the wide variation of the problems used. Although the Legs Problem is more open-ended, it involves concepts and objects that are familiar to most children. In contrast, the Cards Problem requires a multistep solution and the manipulation of relatively large numbers. These two solutions show the importance of assessing children's skills with a variety of problems. Using only a few problems to evaluate children's performance can generate misleading results. A far better approach involves maintaining a portfolio of work over an extended period.

Tim's solution to the Cards Problem also exposes the potential of calculators to affect children's problem-solving efforts. Some children may be tempted to rely on the calculator to do their thinking for them. Although Tim has correctly solved the first step in this problem, he stops when he has an answer on the calculator.

Finally, you may recall Tim's statement in chapter 5: "I drawed it in my head." Since Tim seems unaware of some information contained in the original problem, the fact that he could not reproduce this mental picture is unfortunate. In such situations, an interview might help to clarify the child's depth of understanding.

# BEN

## Legs Problem

4 CWZ

**4 cows**

## Cards Problem

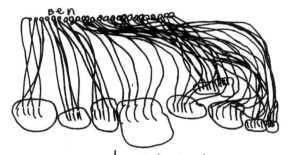

IJroapeKshr OfOLOfthe carDsIn a PaaCKage ⁹ Packa aes.

I drew a picture of all of the cards in a package
9 packages.

# MATHEMATICS PROBLEM-SOLVING SCORING GUIDE

| Conceptual Understanding | Process and Strategies | Communication | Dispositions |
|---|---|---|---|
| Interpreting the concepts of the task and translating them into mathematics | Choosing strategies that can work, then carrying them out | Using pictures, symbols, and words to convey the path to the solution | Attitudes and beliefs of a successful problem solver |
| **What?** | **How?** | **Connecting Path** | **Guiding Light** |
| (A) Translation of the task is enhanced through connections with, or extensions to, other mathematical ideas. | (A) Elegant, complex, or enhanced mathematical processes or strategies are completed. | (A) The connecting path is enhanced by graphics or examples, allowing the reader to easily make connections from one thought to another. | (A) Seeks out feedback, takes risks, and builds collaborative relationships. |
| (B) Translation of the task into mathematical concepts is thoroughly developed. | (B) Pictures, models, diagrams, or symbols are thoroughly developed. | (B) The path that connects concepts, strategies, or verification of the solution is thoroughly developed. | (B) Offers useful feedback, accepts suggestions, and displays confidence. |
| (C) Translation of the task into mathematical concepts is complete. | (C) Pictures, models, diagrams, or symbols are complete. | (C) The path that connects concepts, strategies, or verification of the solution is complete. | (C) Actively engages in classroom discourse, listens attentively, shares ideas, and reflects on the ideas of others. |
| (D) Translation of the task into mathematical concepts is partially complete. | (D) Pictures, models, diagrams, or symbols are only partially complete or partially useful. | (D) The path that connects concepts, strategies, or verification of the solution is only partially displayed. | (D) Builds cooperative relationships, asks clarifying questions, and recognizes the positive aspects of mistakes. |
| (E) Translation of the task into mathematical concepts is underdeveloped or flawed. | (E) Pictures, models, diagrams, or symbols are underdeveloped or flawed. | (E) The path that connects concepts, strategies, or verification of the solution is underdeveloped or sketchy. | (E) Recognizes that learning requires personal effort, patience, perseverance, and a positive attitude. |
| (F) Translation of the task uses inappropriate concepts or shows minimal understanding. | (F) Pictures, models, diagrams, or symbols are ineffective, not evident, or in conflict with solution. | (F) The path that connects concepts, strategies, or verification of the solution is ineffective or not evident. | (F) Flexibility, perseverance, and a positive attitude are absent in the solution process. |

## ACCURACY

| (5) The answer is mathematically justifiable and supported by the work. | (4) The answer is adequate or contains only a minor error. | (1) The answer is incorrect, incomplete, or conflicts with the work. |
|---|---|---|

Legs Problem      Cards Problem

Ben's solution to the Legs Problem is typical of beginning problem solvers (see chapter 2). Although he demonstrated a lack of flexibility by repeatedly using an unsuccessful counting strategy, he displayed perseverance and creativity in finally arriving at an answer.

Ben's solution to the Cards Problem is much more clear and complete, showing that he has made real growth as a problem solver. Although he makes one counting error, his solution reveals that he has understood the problem. I do not contend that correct answers are unimportant. When scoring children's solutions, however, we should consider a sound process to be at least as important as a correct answer.

Ben's solution also reveals the difficulty children may have in describing their solution processes in words. Although he has successfully communicated his solution path with a drawing, his ability to communicate using a written narrative would have received a much lower score.

Ben's patience and perseverance in solving the Cards Problem were commendable. During class, he made three different drawings before finding one to his satisfaction. These general characteristics will be very useful to him in solving a wide range of problems. Over time, they may prove more important than any particular mathematical skill or problem-solving strategy that he might learn.

# TRISTA

## Legs Problem

Anser 1 pig
1 cow
1 horse      I drew 14 legs and
1 chikun      cownted 4 animuls.

Answer  1 pig
        1 cow
        1 horse      I drew 14 legs and
        1 chicken     counted 4 animals.

## Cards Problem

5   10   2
10   20   4
15   30   6
20   40   8
25   50   10

I think it is hard crs i had so
many kids. S i doo 5 kids and 2 cards in thr
pakt not in thr hed like Brit thinks. I
had a lst so you can se 10 pakjs.

I think it is hard (be)cause I had so
many kids. So I drew 5 kids and 2 cards in their
pocket not in their head like Brett thinks. I
made a list so you can see 10 packages.

## MATHEMATICS PROBLEM-SOLVING SCORING GUIDE

| Conceptual Understanding | Process and Strategies | Communication | Dispositions |
|---|---|---|---|
| Interpreting the concepts of the task and translating them into mathematics | Choosing strategies that can work, then carrying them out | Using pictures, symbols, and words to convey the path to the solution | Attitudes and beliefs of a successful problem solver |
| **What?** | **How?** | **Connecting Path** | **Guiding Light** |
| (A) Translation of the task is enhanced through connections with, or extensions to, other mathematical ideas. | (A) Elegant, complex, or enhanced mathematical processes or strategies are completed. | (A) The connecting path is enhanced by graphics or examples, allowing the reader to easily make connections from one thought to another. | (A) Seeks out feedback, takes risks, and builds collaborative relationships. |
| (B) Translation of the task into mathematical concepts is thoroughly developed. | (B) Pictures, models, diagrams, or symbols are thoroughly developed. | (B) The path that connects concepts, strategies, or verification of the solution is thoroughly developed. | (B) Offers useful feedback, accepts suggestions, and displays confidence. |
| (C) Translation of the task into mathematical concepts is complete. | (C) Pictures, models, diagrams, or symbols are complete. | (C) The path that connects concepts, strategies, or verification of the solution is complete. | (C) Actively engages in classroom discourse, listens attentively, shares ideas, and reflects on the ideas of others. |
| (D) Translation of the task into mathematical concepts is partially complete. | (D) Pictures, models, diagrams, or symbols are only partially complete or partially useful. | (D) The path that connects concepts, strategies, or verification of the solution is only partially displayed. | (D) Builds cooperative relationships, asks clarifying questions, and recognizes the positive aspects of mistakes. |
| (E) Translation of the task into mathematical concepts is underdeveloped or flawed. | (E) Pictures, models, diagrams, or symbols are underdeveloped or flawed. | (E) The path that connects concepts, strategies, or verification of the solution is underdeveloped or sketchy. | (E) Recognizes that learning requires personal effort, patience, perseverance, and a positive attitude. |
| (F) Translation of the task uses inappropriate concepts or shows minimal understanding. | (F) Pictures, models, diagrams, or symbols are ineffective, not evident, or in conflict with solution. | (F) The path that connects concepts, strategies, or verification of the solution is ineffective or not evident. | (F) Flexibility, perseverance, and a positive attitude are absent in the solution process. |

## ACCURACY

| (5) The answer is mathematically justifiable and supported by the work. | (4) The answer is adequate or contains only a minor error. | (1) The answer is incorrect, incomplete, or conflicts with the work. |
|---|---|---|

Legs Problem        Cards Problem

Note: To encourage readers to practice with scoring guides, the next three examples—from Trista, Patrick, and Brett—have not been scored using all the criteria in the rubric. If you are unfamiliar with the use of scoring guides, you may wish to use the questions provided after each solution to guide your responses. After you are done scoring each solution, you can compare your scores with those shown at the end of this appendix.

A comparison of Trista's solutions for these two problems demonstrates that she has made significant growth as a problem solver. Her written narrative on the latter problem is more complete, and she no longer feels compelled to use realistic drawings.

- Although her drawings are detailed and accurate, is either of her solutions underdeveloped?
- Has she shown "connections or extensions to other mathematical ideas"?
- Does her path to the answer contain gaps that must be inferred?
- Has Trista thoroughly developed her ideas?
- Are her solutions complete?

# PATRICK

## Legs Problem

I made a list and crossed out the ones I had. I checked with a number sentence to make 14.

## Cards Problem

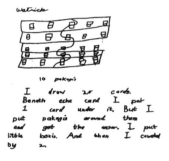

I drew 25 cards beneath each card I put 1 card under it. But I put packages around them and got the answer. I put little boxes and then I counted by 2.

# MATHEMATICS PROBLEM-SOLVING SCORING GUIDE

| Conceptual Understanding | Process and Strategies | Communication | Dispositions |
|---|---|---|---|
| Interpreting the concepts of the task and translating them into mathematics | Choosing strategies that can work, then carrying them out | Using pictures, symbols, and words to convey the path to the solution | Attitudes and beliefs of a successful problem solver |
| **What?** | **How?** | **Connecting Path** | **Guiding Light** |
| (A) Translation of the task is enhanced through connections with, or extensions to, other mathematical ideas. | (A) Elegant, complex, or enhanced mathematical processes or strategies are completed. | (A) The connecting path is enhanced by graphics or examples, allowing the reader to easily make connections from one thought to another. | (A) Seeks out feedback, takes risks, and builds collaborative relationships. |
| (B) Translation of the task into mathematical concepts is thoroughly developed. | (B) Pictures, models, diagrams, or symbols are thoroughly developed. | (B) The path that connects concepts, strategies, or verification of the solution is thoroughly developed. | (B) Offers useful feedback, accepts suggestions, and displays confidence. |
| (C) Translation of the task into mathematical concepts is complete. | (C) Pictures, models, diagrams, or symbols are complete. | (C) The path that connects concepts, strategies, or verification of the solution is complete. | (C) Actively engages in classroom discourse, listens attentively, shares ideas, and reflects on the ideas of others. |
| (D) Translation of the task into mathematical concepts is partially complete. | (D) Pictures, models, diagrams, or symbols are only partially complete or partially useful. | (D) The path that connects concepts, strategies, or verification of the solution is only partially displayed. | (D) Builds cooperative relationships, asks clarifying questions, and recognizes the positive aspects of mistakes. |
| (E) Translation of the task into mathematical concepts is underdeveloped or flawed. | (E) Pictures, models, diagrams, or symbols are underdeveloped or flawed. | (E) The path that connects concepts, strategies, or verification of the solution is underdeveloped or sketchy. | (E) Recognizes that learning requires personal effort, patience, perseverance, and a positive attitude. |
| (F) Translation of the task uses inappropriate concepts or shows minimal understanding. | (F) Pictures, models, diagrams, or symbols are ineffective, not evident, or in conflict with solution. | (F) The path that connects concepts, strategies, or verification of the solution is ineffective or not evident. | (F) Flexibility, perseverance, and a positive attitude are absent in the solution process. |

## ACCURACY

| (5) The answer is mathematically justifiable and supported by the work. | (4) The answer is adequate or contains only a minor error. | (1) The answer is incorrect, incomplete, or conflicts with the work. |
|---|---|---|

Legs Problem    Cards Problem

Although many children solve the Legs Problem by drawing pictures of animals, Patrick has chosen to use a list with a key. He has also used number sentences to verify his work.

- Has Patrick thoroughly developed his solution?
- Is his list complete?
- Is his solution path complete?
- Does Patrick use a higher level of thinking when he solves the problem using generic animals (5 twos) instead of determining what specific animals might be in the barn?
- When you look at Patrick's solution for the Cards Problem, does his drawing show insight that is missing in the other solutions to this problem?
- Is Patrick's drawing complete, thorough, or elegant?
- Has Patrick shown connections with, or extensions to, other mathematical ideas?

# BRETT

## Legs Problem

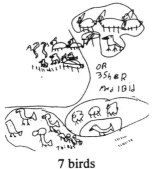

OR
3 sheep
and 1 bird

or
3 sheep
and 1 bird

7 birds

## Cards Problem

i went 5 10 15 20 25 bkus
Les five in a patio
and pot 2 4 6 8 10 abuv it bkus
each pirun sit 2 and Got
the ansr

2 4 6 8 10 Rarar
5 10 15 20 25

I went 5 10 15 20 25 because
(it) has five in a package
and put 2 4 6 8 10 above it because
each person get(s) 2 and got
the answer.

---

# MATHEMATICS PROBLEM SOLVING SCORING GUIDE

| Conceptual Understanding | Process and Strategies | Communication | Dispositions |
|---|---|---|---|
| Interpreting the concepts of the task and translating them into mathematics | Choosing strategies that can work, then carrying them out | Using pictures, symbols, and words to convey the path to the solution | Attitudes and beliefs of a successful problem solver |
| **What?** | **How?** | **Connecting Path** | **Guiding Light** |
| (A) Translation of the task is enhanced through connections with, or extensions to, other mathematical ideas. | (A) Elegant, complex, or enhanced mathematical processes or strategies are completed. | (A) The connecting path is enhanced by graphics or examples, allowing the reader to easily make connections from one thought to another. | (A) Seeks out feedback, takes risks, and builds collaborative relationships. |
| (B) Translation of the task into mathematical concepts is thoroughly developed. | (B) Pictures, models, diagrams, or symbols are thoroughly developed. | (B) The path that connects concepts, strategies, or verification of the solution is thoroughly developed. | (B) Offers useful feedback, accepts suggestions, and displays confidence. |
| (C) Translation of the task into mathematical concepts is complete. | (C) Pictures, models, diagrams, or symbols are complete. | (C) The path that connects concepts, strategies, or verification of the solution is complete. | (C) Actively engages in classroom discourse, listens attentively, shares ideas, and reflects on the ideas of others. |
| (D) Translation of the task into mathematical concepts is partially complete. | (D) Pictures, models, diagrams, or symbols are only partially complete or partially useful. | (D) The path that connects concepts, strategies, or verification of the solution is only partially displayed. | (D) Builds cooperative relationships, asks clarifying questions, and recognizes the positive aspects of mistakes. |
| (E) Translation of the task into mathematical concepts is underdeveloped or flawed. | (E) Pictures, models, diagrams, or symbols are underdeveloped or flawed. | (E) The path that connects concepts, strategies, or verification of the solution is underdeveloped or sketchy. | (E) Recognizes that learning requires personal effort, patience, perseverance, and a positive attitude. |
| (F) Translation of the task uses inappropriate concepts or shows minimal understanding. | (F) Pictures, models, diagrams, or symbols are ineffective, not evident, or in conflict with solution. | (F) The path that connects concepts, strategies, or verification of the solution is ineffective or not evident. | (F) Flexibility, perseverance, and a positive attitude are absent in the solution process. |

## ACCURACY

| (5) The answer is mathematically justifiable and supported by the work. | (4) The answer is adequate or contains only a minor error. | (1) The answer is incorrect, incomplete, or conflicts with the work. |
|---|---|---|

Legs Problem    Cards Problem

During the classroom discussion of the Legs Problem, Brett indicated that he had not labeled one of his answers (two snakes, two pigs, and three birds).

- Has Brett adequately translated the task into mathematical concepts, or is the task partially complete?
- Are his pictures complete or partially recorded?
- In the classroom discussion of the Cards Problem, Brett indicated that the top row of numbers in his solution counts by twos because "they each get two," whereas the bottom row counts by fives because the problem "has five in a package." Did Brett actually solve the problem, or did he simply get lucky?
- Will Brett's way work for other problems? For example, suppose that twenty-four children each receive three cards and that each package contains four cards.
- Does changing the number of cards that each child receives compromise Brett's strategy?
- Will Brett's way work if the number of cards in a package is not a multiple of the number of children in the room?

## SCORES FOR TRISTA'S, PATRICK'S, AND BRETT'S SOLUTIONS

Trista: Legs Problem—Conceptual Understanding (D), Process and Strategies (D), Communication (D); Cards Problem—Conceptual Understanding (B); Process and Strategies (B); Communication (B).

Patrick: Legs Problem—Conceptual Understanding (B), Process and Strategies (B), Communication (B); Cards Problem—Conceptual Understanding (B), Process and Strategies (B), Communication (B).

Brett: Legs Problem—Conceptual Understanding (C), Process and Strategies (C), Communication (D); Cards Problem—Conceptual Understanding (C), Process and Strategies (C), Communication (D).

# Appendix 7
## Checklists for Problem Solving

## A Checklist for a Problem-Solving Classroom

| Discovery | Often | Sometimes | Rarely |
|---|---|---|---|
| Do children and teachers view mathematics as primarily a sense-making activity, solving problems in ways that make sense to them and others? | | | |
| Do children and teachers take time to focus on understanding the mathematical ideas embedded in problems, using reason to uncover these ideas? | | | |
| Do children and teachers pay attention to the process of solving problems, recording their solutions along with the answers? | | | |
| Do children and teachers value different ways of solving a problem, using other solutions to deepen their own understanding? | | | |
| Do children and teachers seek or avoid giving too much help? Do they seek help only when it is genuinely needed? | | | |
| Do children and teachers look for mathematical connections and patterns? Do they employ useful strategies when solutions are not immediately apparent? | | | |
| **Discourse** | | | |
| Do children and teachers share and compare ideas in a non-judgmental manner, offering constructive criticism? | | | |
| Do children and teachers use effective oral and written communication skills, describing their solution processes clearly and completely? | | | |
| Do children and teachers listen to each other, building on the thoughts of others and transforming them into ideas of their own? | | | |
| **Dispositions** | | | |
| Do children and teachers model the characteristics of a successful problem solver—practicing collaboration, patience, perseverance, positive attitude, flexibility, and fluency? | | | |
| Do children and teachers trust one another, taking risks and accepting mistakes as part of the learning process? | | | |
| Do children and teachers practice learning as an ongoing, never-ending journey? | | | |

# A Teacher's Checklist for Use in a Problem-Solving Classroom

## In what ways are mathematical problems worthwhile and challenging?

- Do they require children to use sound and significant mathematics?
- Do they incorporate children's understandings, interests, and experiences?
- Do they develop children's mathematical understandings and skills?
- Do they stimulate children to make connections and to develop a framework for mathematical ideas?
- Do they promote communication about mathematics?

## In what ways do you orchestrate discourse?

- Do you pose questions and tasks that elicit, engage, and challenge children's thinking?
- Do you listen carefully to children's ideas?
- Do you ask children to clarify and justify their ideas orally and in writing?
- Do you decide what to pursue among the ideas that children bring up during discussion?
- Do you decide when and how to attach mathematical notation and language to children's ideas?
- Do you decide when to provide information, when to clarify, when to model, when to lead, and when to let children struggle?
- Do you monitor children's participation in discussions and decide when and how to encourage each child to participate?

## In what ways do you promote discourse among children?

- Do children listen to, respond to, and question the teacher and one another?
- Do children use a variety of tools to reason, make connections, solve problems, and communicate?

- Do children make conjectures and present solutions?
- Do children explore examples and counterexamples to investigate conjectures?
- Do children try to convince themselves and one another of the validity of a particular representation, solution, conjecture, or answer?
- Do children rely on mathematical evidence and argument to determine validity?

## In what ways do you enhance discourse among children?

- Do you encourage the use of computers, calculators, and other technology?
- Do you give children access to concrete materials used as models?
- Do you encourage children to use pictures, diagrams, tables, and graphs?
- Do you encourage children to use invented and conventional terms and symbols?

## In what ways do you create a learning environment that fosters problem solving?

- Do you allow the time necessary for children to explore sound mathematics and grapple with significant ideas and problems?
- Do you use physical space and materials in ways that facilitate children's learning?
- Do you respect and value children's ideas, ways of thinking, and mathematical dispositions?
- Do you encourage children to take intellectual risks?
- Do children value mistakes as learning opportunities?

## In what ways do you assess learning?

- Do you observe, listen to, and gather information about what children are learning?
- Do you examine the effects of tasks, discourse, and the learning environment on children's mathematical knowledge, skills, and dispositions?

Adapted from *Professional Standards for Teaching Mathematics* (NCTM 1991)

# REFERENCES

Andrini, Beth, and Spencer Kagan. *Cooperative Learning and Mathematics.* San Juan Capistrano, Calif.: Resources for Teachers, 1989.

Bach, Richard. *Out of My Mind.* New York: Dell, 1999.

Battista, Michael T. "Teacher Beliefs and the Reform Movement in Mathematics Education." *Phi Delta Kappan* (February 1994): 462–69.

———. "The Mathematical Miseducation of America's Youth: Ignoring Research and Scientific Study in Education." *Phi Delta Kappan* (February 1999): 425–33.

Bosse, Nancy. *Writing Mathematics Grades 1–6.* Mountain View, Calif.: Creative Publications, 1995.

Brannan, Richard, and Oscar Schaaf. *Problem Solving in Mathematics: The Lane County Mathematics Project.* Palo Alto, Calif.: Dale Seymour Publications, 1991.

Britz, Joan, and Norma Richard. *Problem Solving in the Early Childhood Classroom.* Washington, D.C.: National Education Association, 1992.

Brooks, Jacqueline Grennon. and Martin G. Brooks. *In Search of Understanding: The Case for Constructivist Classrooms.* Alexandria, Va.: Association for Supervision and Curriculum Development, 1993.

Brownell, William A. "The Measurement of Understanding." In *The Forty-Fifth Yearbook of the National Society for the Study of Education, Part 1,* edited by N. B. Henry, pp. 138–74. Chicago: University of Chicago Press, 1946.

Brummett, Micaelia Randolph, and Linda Holden. *Story Problems on Their Own: Addition and Subtraction.* Sunnyvale, Calif.: Creative Publications, 1988.

Burns, Marilyn. *About Teaching Mathematics.* White Plains, N.Y.: Cuisenaire Co. of America, 1992.

———. "Arithmetic: The Last Holdout." *Phi Delta Kappan* (February 1994): 471–76.

———. *Writing in Math Class.* White Plains, N.Y.: Cuisenaire Co. of America, 1995.

———. *Math: Facing an American Phobia.* Sausalito, Calif.: Math Solutions, 1998.

Buschman, Larry. "Windows on Learning: Portfolios, Part III, Taking an Integrated Approach." *Learning 93* (January 1993): 22–25.

———. "Sometimes Less Is More." *Arithmetic Teacher* 41 (March 1994): 378–80.

———. "Communicating in the Language of Mathematics." *Teaching Children Mathematics* 1 (February 1995): 324–29.

———. "A Teacher's Journal: Boy, Do I Have Problems!" *Teaching Children Mathematics* 3 (November 1996): 148–54.

———. "Research, Reflection, Practice: Using Student Interviews to Guide Classroom Instruction: An Action Research Project." *Teaching Children Mathematics* 8 (December 2001): 222–27.

Caine, Renate Nummela, and Geoffrey Caine. *Making Connections: Teaching and the Human Brain.* Alexandria, Va.: Association for Supervision and Curriculum Development, 1991.

Cambourne, Brian. *The Whole Story: Natural Learning and the Acquisition of Literacy in the Classroom.* New York: Ashton Scholastic, 1988.

Carpenter, Thomas P., Elizabeth Fennema, Megan Loef Franke, Linda Levi, and Susan Empson. *Children's Mathematics: Cognitively Guided Instruction.* Portsmouth, N.H.: Heinemann, 1999.

Chambers, Donald. "Improving Instruction by Listening to Children." *Teaching Children Mathematics* 1 (February 1995): 378–80.

Charles, Randall. *Problem Solving Experiences in Mathematics: Grades K–8.* Menlo Park, Calif.: Addison-Wesley Publishing Co., 1996.

Charles, Randall, and Frank Lester. *Teaching Problem Solving: What, Why, and How.* Palo Alto, Calif.: Dale Seymour Publications, 1982.

Charles, Randall, and Joanne Lobato. *Future Basics: Developing Numerical Power.* Golden, Colo.: National Council of Supervisors of Mathematics, 1998.

Cobb, Paul. "Where Is the Mind? Constructivist and Sociocultural Perspectives on Mathematical Development." *Educational Researcher* (October 1994): 13–20.

Copley, Juanita V., ed. *Mathematics in the Early Years.* Reston, Va.: National Council of Teachers of Mathematics, 1999.

Covey, Stephen. *The Seven Habits of Highly Effective People: Restoring the Character Ethic.* New York: Simon & Schuster, 1989.

Dewey, John. *How We Think: A Restatement of the Relation of Reflective Thinking to the Educative Process.* Boston, Mass.: Henry Holt, 1933.

Devlin, Keith. *Life by the Numbers.* New York: John Wiley & Sons, 1998.

Folkson, Susan. "Who's Behind the Fence? Creating a Rich Learning Environment with a Nontraditional Problem." *Teaching Children Mathematics* 1 (February 1995): 382–85.

Forsten, Char. *Teaching Thinking and Problem Solving in Math: Strategies, Problems, and Activities.* New York: Scholastic, 1992.

Fosnot, Catherine Twomey, and Maarten Dolk. *Young Mathematicians at Work: Constructing Number Sense, Addition, and Subtraction (Volume 1).* Portsmouth, N.H.: Heinemann, 2001.

———. *Young Mathematicians at Work: Constructing Multiplication and Division (Volume 2).* Portsmouth, N.H.: Heinemann, 2001.

———. *Young Mathematicians at Work: Constructing Fractions, Decimals, and Percents (Volume 3).* Portsmouth, N.H.: Heinemann, 2001.

Gardner, Howard. *Multiple Intelligences: The Theory in Practice*. New York: Basic Books, 1993.

Goleman, Daniel. *Emotional Intelligence: Why It Can Matter More Than IQ*. New York: Bantam Books, 1995.

Gozdz, Kazimierz, ed. *Community Building: Renewing Spirit and Learning in Business*. San Francisco, Calif.: New Leaders Press, 1995.

Graves, Donald. *Breaking Ground: Teachers Relate Reading and Writing in the Elementary School*. Portsmouth, N.H.: Heinemann, 1985.

Griffiths, Richard, and Margaret Clyne. *Language in the Mathematics Classroom: Talking, Representing, Recording*. Portsmouth, N.H.: Heinemann, 1994.

Grouws, Douglas A., ed. *Handbook of Research on Mathematics Teaching and Learning*. New York: Macmillan, 1992.

Hart, Leslie A. *"Anchor" Math*. Village of Oak Creek, Ark.: Books for Education, 1992.

Hiebert, James, Thomas P. Carpenter, Elizabeth Fennema, Karen C. Fuson, Diana Wearne, Hanlie Murray, Alwyn Oliver, and Piet Human. *Making Sense: Teaching and Learning Mathematics with Understanding*. Portsmouth, N.H.: Heinemann, 1997.

Holmes, Dick, Wendy Klassen, and Walter Szetela. *Mathematics: Problem-Solving Activities (Grades 3–6)*. Palo Alto, Calif.: Dale Seymour Publications, 1993.

Hoogeboom, Shirley, and Judy Goodnow. *The Problem Solver 1–6: Activities for Learning Problem-Solving Strategies*. Sunnyvale, Calif.: Creative Publications, 1987.

Jensen, Eric. *Teaching with the Brain in Mind*. Alexandria, Va.: Association for Supervision and Curriculum Development, 1998.

Johnson, Terry, and Daphne Louis. *Bringing It All Together: A Program for Literacy*. Portsmouth, N.H.: Heinemann, 1990.

Kagan, Spencer. *Cooperative Learning*. San Juan Capistrano, Calif.: Resources for Teachers, 1989.

Kamii, Constance. *Young Children Reinvent Arithmetic*. New York: Teachers College Press, 1985.

———. *Young Children Continue to Reinvent Arithmetic, 3rd Grade*. New York: Teachers College Press, 1994.

Kamii, Constance, and Linda Leslie Joseph. *Young Children Continue to Reinvent Arithmetic, 2nd Grade: Implications of Piaget's Theory*. New York: Teachers College Press, 1989.

Kingsolver, Barbara. *The Poisonwood Bible*. New York: Harper Collins, 1998.

Kirk, Dorothy A., ed. *Problem Solving in Math: Computation and Strategies*. Cleveland, Ohio: Modern Curriculum Press, 1983.

Kohn, Alfie. *No Contest: The Case Against Competition*. Boston, Mass.: Houghton Mifflin Co., 1986.

Krulick, Stephen. *A Handbook for Elementary School Teachers: Problem Solving*. Newton, Mass.: Allyn & Bacon, 1988.

Krulick, Stephen, and Jesse A. Rudnick. *Assessing Reasoning and Problem Solving: A Sourcebook for Elementary School Teachers*. Newton, Mass.: Allyn & Bacon, 1998.

Kuhs, Therese M. *Measure for Measure: Using Portfolios in K–8 Mathematics*. Westport, Conn.: Heinemann, 1997.

Labinowicz, Ed. *The Piaget Primer: Thinking, Learning, Teaching*. Menlo Park, Calif.: Addison-Wesley Publishing Co., 1980.

———. *Learning from Children: New Beginnings for Teaching Numerical Thinking: A Piagetian Approach*. Menlo Park, Calif.: Addison-Wesley Publishing Co., 1985.

Lambdin, Diana V., Paul E. Kehle, and Ronald V. Preston. *Emphasis on Assessment: Readings from NCTM's School-Based Journals*. Reston, Va.: National Council of Teachers of Mathematics, 1996.

Lester, Frank K. Jr. "Musings about Mathematical Problem-Solving Research: 1970–1994." *Journal for Research in Mathematics Education* 25 (6) (1994): 660–75.

Lowen, Craig. "Creative Problem Solving." *Teaching Children Mathematics* 2 (October 1995): 96–99.

Maris, Ron. *Better Move On Frog!* London, England: Walker Books, 1989.

Martinez, Michael E. "What Is Problem Solving." *Phi Delta Kappan* 79 (8)(April 1998): 605–9.

Mills, Heidi, Timothy O'Keefe, Lonnie B. Nelson, and David Whitin. *Mathematics in the Making: Authoring Ideas in Primary Classrooms*. Portsmouth, N.H.: Heinemann, 1996.

Moon, Jean, and Linda Schulman. *Finding the Connections: Linking Assessment, Instruction, and Curriculum in Elementary Mathematics*. Westport, Conn.: Heinemann, 1995.

Myren, Christina. "Encouraging Young Children to Solve Problems Independently." *Teaching Children Mathematics* 3 (October 1996): 72–76.

National Council of Teachers of Mathematics (NCTM). *Curriculum and Evaluation Standards for School Mathematics*. Reston, Va.: NCTM, 1989.

———. *Professional Standards for Teaching Mathematics*. Reston, Va.: NCTM, 1991.

———. *Addenda Books K–12 (Series)*. Reston, Va.: NCTM, 1992.

———. *Assessment in the Mathematics Classroom*. 1993 Yearbook of the National Council of Teachers of Mathematics (NCTM), edited by Norman L. Webb. Reston, Va.: NCTM, 1993.

———. *Assessment Standards for School Mathematics*. Reston, Va.: NCTM, 1995.

———. *Communication in Mathematics: K–12 and Beyond*. Reston, Va.: NCTM, 1996.

———. *The Teaching and Learning of Algorithms in School Mathematics*. Reston, Va.: NCTM, 1998.

———. *Principles and Standards for School Mathematics*. Reston, Va.: NCTM, 2000.

National Research Council. *Everybody Counts: A Report to the Nation on the Future of Mathematical Education.* Washington, D.C.: National Academy Press, 1989.

Overton, Patrick. "Faith." In *Making a Living without a Job: Winning Ways for Creating Work That You Love,* by Barbara J. Winter, p. 236. New York: Bantam Doubleday Dell, 1993.

O'Brien, Thomas. "Parrot Math." *Phi Delta Kappan* (February 1999): 434–38.

O'Connell, Susan. *Introduction to Problem Solving: Strategies for the Elementary Math Classroom.* Portsmouth, N.H.: Heinemann, 2000.

O'Daffer, Phares G., ed. *Problem Solving: Tips for Teachers.* Reston, Va.: National Council of Teachers of Mathematics, 1989.

Perkins, David. *Smart Schools: From Training Memories to Educating Minds.* New York: The Free Press, 1995.

Piaget, Jean. *The Construction of Reality in the Child.* 1937. Reprint, New York: Basic Books, 1954.

———. *To Understand Is to Invent.* 1948. Reprint, New York: Grossman, 1973.

Reeves, Charles A. *Problem-Solving Techniques Helpful in Mathematics and Science.* Reston, Va.: National Council of Teachers of Mathematics, 1987.

Reys, Barbara J., and Robert E. Reys. "Computation in the Elementary Curriculum: Shifting the Emphasis." *Teaching Children Mathematics* 5 (December 1998): 236–41.

Richardson, Kathy. *Math Time: The Learning Environment.* Norman, Okla.: Educational Enrichment, 1997.

———. "Too Easy for Kindergarten and Just Right for First Grade." *Teaching Children Mathematics* 3 (April 1997): 432–37.

Routman, Regie. *Invitations: Changing as Teachers and Learners K–12.* Portsmouth, N.H.: Heinemann, 1991.

Sagan, Carl. "Basketball's Lessons for Science." *New York Times Magazine,* 7 November 1993, sec. 8, p. 9.

Schoenfeld, Alan. H. "Learning to Think Mathematically: Problem Solving, Metacognition, and Sense Making in Mathematics." *Handbook of Research on Mathematics Teaching and Learning,* edited by Douglas A. Grouws, pp. 334–70. New York: Macmillan, 1992.

Schwartz, Sydney L., and Anna Beth Brown. "Communicating with Young Children in Mathematics: A Unique Challenge." *Teaching Children Mathematics* 1 (February 1995): 350–53.

Simonsen, Linda M., and Anne R. Teppo. "Using Alternative Algorithms with Preservice Teachers." *Teaching Children Mathematics* 5 (May 1999): 516–19.

Smith, Frank. *Reading without Nonsense.* Portsmouth, N.H.: Heinemann, 1985.

———. *Between Hope and Havoc: Essays into Human Learning and Education.* Portsmouth, N.H.: Heinemann, 1995.

Steen, Lynn Arthur. *Why Numbers Count: Quantitative Literacy for Tomorrow's America.* New York: The College Board, 1997.

Stenmark, Jean. *101 Short Problems.* Berkeley, Calif.: EQUALS, 1995.

Stigler, James W., and James Hiebert. "Understanding and Improving Classroom Mathematics Instruction: An Overview of the TIMSS Video Study." *Phi Delta Kappan* (September 1997): 14–21.

Sylwester, Robert. *A Celebration of Neurons: An Educator's Guide to the Human Brain.* Alexandria, Va.: Association for Supervision and Curriculum Development, 1995.

Trafton, Paul R., and Diane Thiessen. *Learning through Problems: Number Sense and Computational Strategies.* Portsmouth, N.H.: Heinemann, 1999.

Wand, Jennifer. "Who Will Be First?" *Teaching Children Mathematics* 2 (December 1995): 214–15.

Wheatley, Grayson. *Quick Draw: Developing Spatial Sense in Mathematics.* Tallahassee, Fla.: Mathematics Learning, 1996.

Wiggins, Grant. "Creating Tests Worth Taking." *Educational Leadership* (May 1992): 26–33.

Wiggins, Grant, and Jay McTighe. *Understanding by Design.* Alexandria, Va.: Association for Supervision and Curriculum Development, 1998.

Winograd, Ken, and Karen M. Higgins. "Writing, Reading, and Talking Mathematics: One Interdisciplinary Possibility." *The Reading Teacher* (December 1994/January 1995): 310–17.

# RESOURCES

Creative Publications, 5623 West 115th Street, Worth, IL 60482-9931.

Talents Unlimited, Sara Waldrop, 1107 Arlington Street, Mobile, AL 36606.